To my life partner and best friend, love you feo!

ISBN 978-0-9982144-0-5
Illustration & Design by Natalia Swarz, www.nataliaswarz.com
Editing by Valerie Gramling
Photography by Valerie Lopez, www.devlopz.com
Printing logistics by Daniela Sandoval

This book is not intended as a substitute for the medical advice of physicians. The reader should consult a physician in matters relating to her health and particularly with respect to any symptoms that may require diagnosis or medical attention. The intention of this book is to give friendly advice and information for the reader to make better decisions regarding her health and lifestyle when pregnant. Likewise readers are advised to take full responsibility for their safety and know their limits. Before practicing the skills described in this book, be sure that your environment is safe, and do not take risks beyond your level of experience, aptitude, training, and comfort.

32 WEEKS
Mural by @cr_eatestudio

Ok, so having a baby was on the bottom (or not at all) of my priority list. But in life, things happen in a weird way, the way they have to. For me, being anal retentive, obsessed with planning and knowing everything, my totally unexpected pregnancy put me into a state of mental shock for two weeks (ok, I think it lasted until I felt a little butterfly moving in my belly! It was really happening, the miracle of life).

So there I was, just married (in the civil way), with a postponed religious wedding, with a thousand and one entrepreneur plans and ideas, and scared crazy. But luckily enough I was surrounded with the best energy and love from my family and close friends.

After long days of meditation, I accepted it was ok not having control over everything that happens in my life. I realized how fortunate I actually was and how grateful I had to be for that little bean that got a spark of life against all odds.

For those who don't know me (which I really hope is a lot of you, meaning someone other than my mom and sisters actually bought this book!!!), I'm a complete food enthusiast, I LOVE food, real food, the kind that leaves your body full of energy, happiness and love.

I'm also crazy about cooking. I consider myself pretty much a self-taught chef; it only takes creativity, passion and love! I cook for my husband, family and friends (and now for my business...my super cute brand called Food from the Heart!). I love putting all my good vibes and energy into everything I prepare, no matter how simple it is. It's this energy that makes a difference not only in taste but in how good it makes you feel after eating it. I love looking at meals as magical moments that bring people together but it is much more! Food for me is a way of healing, nourishing and balancing the body!

I thought it would be super cool to compile all my pregnancy tips regarding a fun, active, healthy and real pregnancy for super powerful and chic mommas-to-be out there.

I hope you like it!! It was all done from the heart!

Table of Contents

RECIPES: LET'S GET HANDS TO WORK!

STAYING ACTIVE

PREPARING FOR BABY'S ARRIVAL

EXTRA GOODIES LINK

www.ffthmiami.com/extra-goodies

Password: MOMMYLOVE

Free EXTRA goodies for you to download! YAY! ♡

1. Quick & Dirty Lifesaving Tips

What follows are my
SUPER COOL and SUPER
HANDY "must-knows" and
"must-dos" for each trimester
on this awesome journey!

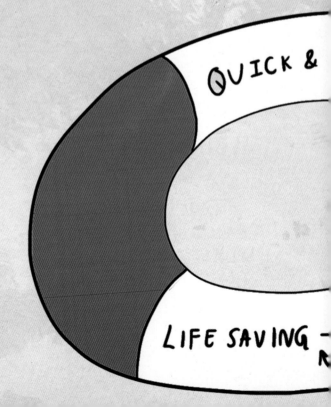

QUICK &

LIFE SAVING –
R

TIPS

First
TRIMESTER
(1-12 weeks)

PRENATAL VITAMINS

As soon as you find out you are pregnant start taking your prenatals! If you are lucky enough to find out by the first weeks of conception, congrats! That's a great way to start taking care of your little one! (In my case I found out I was pregnant after months of back to back trips, some good cocktails and even horse-riding parties.) If you have been planning to get pregnant even better! Start now. Please go for the most natural option on the market, containing non-Genetically Modified Organisms (non-GMOs), organic and with Docosahexaenoic acid, an omega-3 fatty acid (DHA). I also strongly recommend you start taking cod liver oil (associated with higher birth weights!!) - ask your doctor for recommendations!

NO MORE BOOZE

Stop alcohol consumption. Some doctors approve of having a maximum of two glasses of wine or champagne a week. In my case I waited until my second trimester to have an occasional glass of happiness! Once every week or at special celebrations only. The baby is more vulnerable to brain damage and birth defects during the first trimester, so please do wait until the second trimester. I think is not worth risking your baby's health, so I recommend leaving that quota for your birthday or a very special date or a very bad craving for pairing your meal with wine!

STAY AWAY FROM CIGARETTES

If you are a smoker, the ideal moment to quit is before getting pregnant. Please try to stay away from smokers. Second-hand smoke also increases your risk of miscarriage.

FOOD DON'TS

As soon as you find out you are expecting, it's important to prevent harmful bacteria such as listeria and salmonella in your food. Listeria, even thought it is very rare, can potentially cause a risk to your baby. On the other hand, salmonella will only make you sick (vomiting even more, diarrhea, headaches, etc.) so it's better to prevent it all together by suspending the following foods:

✕ Raw or undercooked eggs, meat and poultry

✕ Raw sushi or any food containing raw fish

✕ Smoked seafood

✕ Oysters

✕ Fish containing high levels of mercury (shark, mackerel, swordfish, tuna)

✕ Pâtés

✕ Unpasteurized dairy

✕ Soft cheeses such as blue, brie, camembert

✕ Unpasteurized versions of the following cheeses:

cottage, mozzarella, feta, cream cheese, ricotta, goat cheese

✕ Deli meats

✕ Non-organic veggies especially tomatoes and leafy greens (See The Dirty Dozen™ and The Clean

Fifteen™ produce lists for veggies containing more pesticides)

✕ Limit your caffeine consumption to maximum 2 cups of coffee/caffeinated tea a day

✕ Unwashed fruits and vegetables.

If you are a junk food lover, please please stop your soft drink, fast food, and processed food consumption!!! Just start one step at a time. For example, replacing sodas with water is a great start!

Decide whether you are staying with your OBGYN and the traditional hospital experience or if you want to look into the midwife and birth center world. It is your experience and you should own it! Don't let anyone make decisions for you, so get informed and really decide what best fits your expectations and values. The second option usually provides a greater emphasis on going as natural as possible, meaning no meds, natural birth of course, and the use of birthing pools; the service of doulas is also very common. These are women who support the whole labor process not only emotionally but with exercises, massages, relaxation and breathing techniques that help you cope with pain as no traditional medicine is used. Doula services can also be hired for hospital labors; some hospitals don't allow it though, so check with your hospital first.

Please take no offense if you think differently from what I'm about to say. It is just my humble and honest opinion! ♡

In my case I knew that I wanted a natural birth no matter what. First, because of the connection of giving birth naturally; being able to help your baby get out with your own hands and hold him on your chest is just so magical. Also, babies get thousands of antibodies from the mucus in the birth canal that make them have stronger immune systems, fewer allergies and diseases overall. Secondly, I believe this is the way it has been meant to be since forever, and it's just natural that your baby chooses the day he wants to be born, something which is completely ignored when C-sections are scheduled just to be more convenient for moms and doctors or because people want to avoid pain from contractions and labor. Thirdly, with a natural delivery you can walk minutes after birth! C-section is a major surgery. I think people forget about that. After birth you want to be in the best condition possible so you can take care of your little one.

Nonetheless, it is so difficult to have a birth plan because it can be so unexpected. Anything can happen as every labor is completely different. So what I did was join prenatal yoga classes and start an exercise routine that prepared my hips and muscles for natural birth. Having that in mind, I had the C-section as my last option if something medical came up, because of course this procedure has saved many lives and I completely support it under the right medical reasons, just not superficial and vain ones. For those who wonder, I did have a natural birth but with meds and in a traditional hospital. My doctors and the hospital staff were wonderful; they gave me the time I needed and supported my decisions. But maybe for my next baby I will look more into the birthing center experience (which fascinates me, but it was too late when I considered it).

So in conclusion, as I mentioned above, whatever your opinion on this is, do some research and just own it! Own your experience and choose your support team; it is completely your game, a fun, magical game that will change your life forever!!

DOUBLE CHECK YOUR MEDICATIONS

Consult your doctor if it's safe to take any prescribed medication you are currently taking, and also about the safety of over-the-counter (OTC) medicine. For the first eight weeks avoid any OTC medicine; this is a critical period for irreversible embryo damage. I recommend giving natural remedies such as aromatherapy a try, like peppermint oil massaged on the temples for headaches, ginger teas for flus and lots of water for any ache! For those who are not familiar with aromatherapy it is the use of essential oils to manage pains, congestion and stress. Ask for them in your health store, they usually carry them!

(Tip: I love smelling lavender oil before going to bed. Plus you can use it during labor to calm yourself!!)

CHILLAX

Stop, relax and take your schedule as easy as you can. In the first trimester, especially by week 4, and then again in your last trimester, it's normal to feel extremely tired and sleepy. In the first weeks of conception your body is adjusting to all hormonal changes, and is using all the energy and nutrients necessary to form the placenta and the embryo, so take it easy on yourself and try to prepare your schedule ahead.

30 weeks!

6 weeks... Napping ALL DAY!

29 weeks ~ Baby Shower

29 weeks!

POSTCARD

FROM:

32 weeks / My 25th birthday ♡

Happiness! ♡

31 weeks!

MORNING SICKNESS KILLERS

Hopefully morning sickness and nausea only last for your first trimester. These natural options really helped me survive that miserable state:

- Wearing "Sea bands": these are wristbands with a plastic stud that applies pressure to the Nei Kuan acu-pressure point of each wrist (think of the wristbands used by tennis players to wipe sweat, but in a cute purple color that also cures your nausea!!). They work better if you wear them before the nausea starts. I recommend wearing them as soon as you wake up; that way worked perfectly for me.

- Drinking ginger shots with honey in the morning and as needed throughout the day (see recipe pg.113).

- Avoiding fried foods.

- Not brushing your teeth as soon as you finish eating; wait for 45 min to an hour.

- Crowding out foods that make you sick. One day you will love something and hate it the next! Experiment with savory foods and sweet foods for breakfast to see which you like best; for example, in my first trimester I could only eat sweet breakfasts such as smoothies, oatmeals and porridges.

CRAVINGS ARE NOT THAT REAL IN REAL LIFE

Sorry if I just ruined your inner fatty girl dream but pregnancy is not the time to eat like a piggy and eat all the trashy food in the world. Please keep in mind that all those extra and unneeded pounds you gain are going to be a nightmare to drop.

Also, and most important of all, you need to realize that what you put into your mouth is what your body is going to use to form your baby! If you put in quality foods, the outcome will be of the best quality! Think about how babies' immune systems, allergy propensity and overall health start developing from your prenatal nutrition. Also, good nutrition will help you prevent constipation, hand and feet swelling and mood swings throughout your pregnancy!

Please don't feel tempted to imitate those ladies in the movies, commercials, media, and even some American pregnancy books, which show that it's totally ok for pregnant ladies to have a burger, fries, a coke, and ice cream for dessert just because they had a craving. This is a big No, No!!

Think about it twice, drink some water (cravings are usually gone after a tall glass of water) and start learning how to listen to your body. If you have a "Craving" for something try to deconstruct that craving and give the body what it really needs. Let's say you are craving ice cream; maybe your body is asking for sweetness or something creamy. So you can have a cup of organic, whole fat Greek yogurt topped with some raw unfiltered honey, dates and nuts! Start listening to your body and replace the bad cravings with nutritious ones!

I'm not saying you should never indulge, but just as before you were pregnant, everything is about balance. If you avoid something forever eventually your willpower will break. So my recommendation is to look for the best versions of that food you really want. Look for organic, homemade, non GMOs, good oils, no bad sugars (I'll expand on what are considered bad oils, sugars and more ahead!) and remember that once in a while won't kill you!!! Just like eating one veggie won't make you lose a pound instantly.

FOOD AVERSIONS ARE THE REAL THING

As I just mentioned, cravings are more of a cultural myth than anything, but food aversions do happen. You may love a food today and the next day not even stand the smell. In my case it was raw greens (being a veggie lover my whole life I almost panicked). When I even thought about raw spinach, my stomach started its well-known procedure to evacuate.

Please don't stress, you just have to be patient with your changing body and hormones and experiment with different foods. For me, green juices and smoothies saved my life during my first trimester. I got my veggie daily quota from these yummy drinks! (See recipes ahead!)

HYDRATE YOUR BOOBIES & BELLY

You need to start this ritual before getting pregnant (if it doesn't take you by surprise). I know you are totally afraid of those not so aesthetically-looking stretch marks so it's better to start as soon as possible. Select your products wisely, check for dangerous parabens and metals that are not good for your baby. Go as natural as you can! Pure almond oil or coconut oil does an excellent job.

H2O TO THE MAX

If you are not in the habit of drinking water, your first trimester is a great moment to start. This will help you avoid water retention and swelling in your last trimester. Try going for clean, pure, filtered water. Buy a good filter and carry a stainless steel, glass, or BPA-free plastic bottle with you all the time. Try to avoid store-bought plastic water bottles. Chemicals like Bisphenol-A (BPA) and other obesogens are passed from the bottle to the water. Also remember to stock up on toilet paper; the increased pressure to your bladder will make you pee like craaazy, especially in the last trimester.

MOVE YOUR CUTE, LITTLE, PREGNANT ASS

As with your habit of drinking water, staying active must become a habit if it is not already in your daily routine. This will not only help you control your weight gain but also form a healthy baby and keep you away from emotional swings, swelling and other aches coming later in pregnancy.

Your activity should be moderate; avoid bouncing around with crazy cardio classes. If you can use a heart rate monitor do not exceed 140 beats per minute; if you don't have a heart rate monitor just keep your activity at a level at which you could maintain a conversation without losing your breath. You may not engage in activities that make you lose your balance or hit your belly area.

Exercises such as yoga, Pilates, swimming or walking are great. If you can have a personal instructor specialized in pregnancy training, even better! Meditation is an excellent way of keeping your sanity during these months of changes. This also helps you connect to your baby and will be a great tool during labor. (See "Staying Active" section for stretches, beneficial everyday yoga poses, and meditation.)

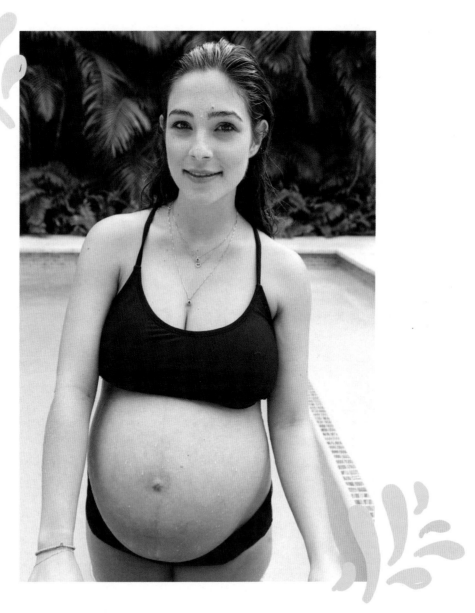

8 weeks

12 weeks

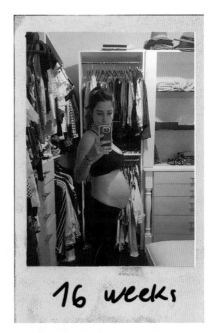

16 weeks

22 weeks

26 weeks

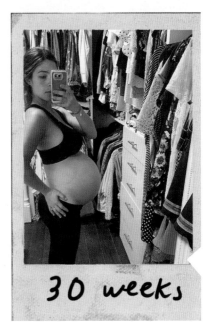

30 weeks

KEEP THOSE MOOD SWINGS UNDER CONTROL

Your significant other, family and close friends will be very grateful if you keep that wild animal inside you very far away. Mood swings are completely normal, caused by hormones, anxiety about the unknown or just because you are so, so tired. Keep that in mind, and as soon as you start having weird thoughts listen to that song you love and start dancing around, take a long bath, give yourself an exfoliation, do your nails, watch that cool movie you love, read your favorite book or cook some yummy healthy treats! (See recipes ahead!) Do whatever it is that you enjoy doing a lot that can keep you away from feeling fearful, stressed or anxious.

KEEP THAT SMILE HEALTHY

During pregnancy all the hormonal changes make us more susceptible to gum disease. So just continue with a healthy routine brushing your teeth after every meal, and don't forget to floss!! That's key especially now that your gums are more sensitive and more prone to bleeding. A healthy lifestyle starts with a clean mouth!! A cool tip from Ayurvedic Medicine (a system of natural healing from India) is to never forget to clean your tongue! In addition to removing toxins and helping your digestion, it also helps get rid of cravings!

START KEEPING TRACK OF YOUR BELLY

It is so wonderful to see with your own eyes the miracle of life, how perfectly the body changes and does things in order to create a human being. This can be documented in pictures! Start a photo diary as soon as you can. Select the same background and a simple outfit (think black pants and black sports bra) to maintain uniformity among the pictures. Take one picture doing the same position every week; at the end put all the pictures together and you will see how awesome your body was through the whole process.

Second
TRIMESTER
(13-27 weeks)

TIME TO CHANGE YOUR BRA

Everyone is different but you should notice your boobies growing fast by this time. Replace your bras for ones that provide more support. Maternity and nursing bras are great, post-augmentation bras work great too, if not better than the others. Remember that you are trying to beat gravity in order to prevent stretch marks!

YOU ARE PREGNANT NOT FAT!

Finally your pregnant belly starts showing a little, and you actually look more pregnant than fat. Style your growing baby bump with cute outfits; feel sexy, beautiful and grateful for having a life inside of you. Sometimes it is mentally difficult to see your body changing so fast, so just be proud of those changes and embrace your changing pregnant body with love and good vibes.

By now everyone, even strange people in the street, may feel tempted to touch your belly (which I personally hated; it's my belly not yours!!!). So when approaching someone try to keep a distance, or place your hand on your belly to discourage those crazy hands. I know you want your husband, family and really close friends to feel the baby kicking, but keep it there! It's only the good energy of people who really love you that you want to approach your belly! In case you can't prevent annoying people from touching your belly, try mentally imagining a light around your body protecting you and your baby. Don't call me crazy, it really works.

MyKonos
15 weeks

☀ "Sun setting & a little
mango growing inside my belly".

PREGNANCY
ANNOUNCEMENT
Instagram Post!

ENERGY BURST

Generally by the end of your first trimester all the nausea and morning sickness is replaced by lots and lots of energy! YAY finally! This was my favorite time; I felt I had my energy back and sometimes forgot I was even pregnant. Use that energy to:

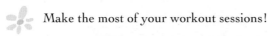 Make the most of your workout sessions!

Plan romantic getaways with your hubby or significant other. It's the safest period of your pregnancy to travel by plane so just go for a weekend or more to this place you always wanted to visit! Remember that after the baby is born you won't be able to travel as much or have the opportunity to share between the two of you a romantic trip for a while.

Start planning everything for your nursery, baby shower and registry. (See "Preparing for Baby's Arrival" section for more ideas.)

ENGAGE IN SOME CHATTING WITH YOUR LITTLE ONE

By the end of this trimester you and your partner can start playing stimulating music to your little one, reading books or that special prayer you love every night. You won't believe how they will recognize your voice when born!

LET'S TRAVEL
THE WORLD
TOGETHER

POSTCARD

PLACE
STAMP
HERE

@ Mykonos,
Greece

15 weeks

Paris
17 weeks

CARTAGENA

ISTANBUL

BODY PILLOW, YOUR NEW BEST FRIEND

Now that your belly is really starting to grow, you will find it very difficult to find a comfy sleeping position without using a fort of pillows. For me it was a challenge because I loved sleeping on my stomach and on my back. On your stomach obviously is no longer an option because of your belly, and sleeping on your back can reduce the circulation of blood to your baby because the belly is putting pressure on the aorta and vena cava.

So the best way to go is to sleep on your side, especially the left side which allows the maximum blood flow. The body pillow will make it easier for you to actually stay on your side. If you are having trouble sleeping caused by exhaustion, leg pain and shortness of breath, try taking a warm bath before bed. Go to bed and talk to the baby, read a story or a prayer. Try breathing techniques and positive thinking meditations; they worked wonderfully for me.

GIVE YOUR SKIN A BREAK

As you know your hormones are all over the place so just relax. Don't be hard on yourself if you are getting unusual pimples here and there, new moles and skin pigmentation; it's all normal. Continue with your daily moisturizer rituals but make sure the products you are using do not contain any chemical, paraben or harsh ingredient (common in anti-wrinkle, antioxidant, and anti-pigment creams). Consult with your dermatologist for safer options. Another great tip is to double the sunscreen application; try three times a day (if you don't have it as part of your face ritual yet) as it will help control skin pigmentation and the appearance of dark spots from the sun.

Oh god, and if a darker line starts marking your belly, it's normal too! Not every woman gets it but if you do, do not worry, it will start fading away after pregnancy. Also, postpartum your skin pigmentation will start to fade and can be treated with your dermatologist's help!

Third
TRIMESTER
(28 weeks to birth)

KEEP IT COOL

You will start feeling completely pregnant by this time with your now noticeable bump, lost energy, and back, leg and all sorts of weird pains, plus extra anxiety because you're almost there! Relax, breathe and take it one step at a time:

- Go back to your first trimester nap schedule if needed.

- Keep your workout sessions running but modify intensity if needed.

- Make stretching and yoga poses a habit these last weeks (see "Staying Active" section).

- Continue with your water consumption, now essential to prevent swelling from water retention. I know this will increase your trips to the restroom even more, but take it easy and try to pee every time you are about to leave the house, or find a clean restroom around, even if you don't feel like it.

MODEL FOR A DAY

Usually it's better to wait until your baby bump is really noticeable to book your maternity photoshoot! I did mine on my 32nd week and it was perfect. Get creative! Choose a place you really like - the beach, a park, your house - and take those pictures that will be worth gold in a few years. I tried to stay away from the classic picture - holding hands in the shape of a heart on the baby bump (please don't get offended if you love that!!) - just because it's really cool to do something different!! I tried experimenting with silhouette pictures; the outcome is gorgeous, give it a try!

i love you sweetheart . . . now it's time for us to rest . . .

GET SOME BUMP WEIGHT OFF YOUR BACK

For the last trimester it's essential that you get yourself a belly support belt, support tanks or bottoms with support fabric. This will not only ease some back pain but it will help you prevent those stretch marks from appearing. Backache can also be controlled with some cool yoga poses! (See "Staying Active" section.)

ACID BURNING YOUR THROAT

For some women this happens earlier in pregnancy, but for sure by now you may experience a lot of heartburn and acid reflux. This is because your poor stomach is completely compressed by your growing uterus. You can control this by eating smaller portions, especially for your last meal of the day. Also there are some yoga heart opening poses that will be of great help (see "Staying Active" section). If you are experiencing this discomfort during the night, try using some pillows to be at a more upright position.

SLEEPLESS NIGHTS

There are different factors that can contribute to those panda eyes the next morning. One common reason is leg cramps. These are easily relieved by stretching your legs and moving your toes in and out. (You have a visual of the movement in the "Staying Active" section!)

Also, now that your baby is really growing, his space is limited so you will feel a lot of movement going on especially at night. I personally loved feeling my baby so active because you know he is strong and healthy, but when this is affecting your sleep it can be a problem. Try rubbing your belly and talking to your baby. Let him know it's time for mommy to sleep and rest; he can hear you and understand you! You are a team, let him know that!

As you get closer to the expected day, anxiety levels may be increasing. If you find yourself wondering at night unable to fall asleep, try breathing slowly and deeply while you thank God or the universe for what you have. Try making a list in your head of the things you are grateful for and with each one take a long breath. By number 3 you will be far gone!

Sign up for childbirth, breastfeeding (the one I found incredibly important!!), and infant CPR classes to increase your knowledge on the topic. This will considerably lower your anxiety as you will be taught lots of useful information. Remember, it is not always a good idea to go online and watch birth videos and read every single article you can find (or listen to everyone's stories about their painful labor). There is a lot of trash out there on the internet and this can lead you to even more anxiety, fear, confusion and stress. Don't try to know it all! It is humanly impossible; for birth and motherhood in general you have to follow your instincts!

MEMO

☐ Labor and Childbirth

☐ Breastfeeding class!!!!

☐ Infant CPR

LOOKING FOR A PEDIATRICIAN

Yes, you need to go shopping for a pediatrician before your baby is born. You will need to give your pediatrician's information when you are checking in for delivery. So start doing your research, call and make prenatal appointments. Things I found important to consider are the following:

- Distance from home!! Crucial for me.

- If they support and give advice about natural remedies before going to actual medicine.

- If it's a single practice or a large practice. Single practice means there is only one doctor, large practice multiple doctors. They both have their pros and cons. Usually a single practice has a more intimate relationship with patients as they will remember you and your preferences easily. The con is possibly longer waiting times when you have to do a walk-in if your little one is sick. On the other hand, a large practice can be less intimate but you can have different points of view and advice. Waiting times for walk-ins are considerably lower because the next free doctor will see you.

- How clean and nice the staff and place is.

- If they have different waiting rooms for sick and well kids.

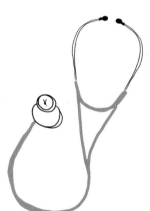

Do not stress over this; go to a couple of prenatal appointments and if you end up not liking the one you chose, you can always change!

PACKING YOUR HOSPITAL BAG

It's better to feel ready so you can be relaxed. I recommend you pack your hospital bag by around week 32. You never know! It's better to be prepared! Having your own things will make you feel more comfortable and have an even more amazing experience.

Here is what I consider just necessary to pack:

- ☑ Two or three button-up front PJ's to have easy access for breastfeeding,
- ☑ Two nursing bras and comfortable underwear,
- ☑ Dark-colored socks that you won't care about if they get ruined,
- ☑ Two loose-fitting outfits for you (sorry to put it this way but you will probably look 4 months pregnant because your uterus is still huge!),
- ☑ Flip-Flops or comfortable shoes that can be easily taken off,
- ☑ Your toiletries (deodorant, shampoo, toothbrush, moisturizer, soap, etc.),
- ☑ Make-up kit (you want to look always nice for pictures!),
- ☑ Good hair bands and clips (I recommend wearing a braid for labor so your hair doesn't get messy),
- ☑ Four PJ's for baby and one take-home outfit,
- ☑ Nursing pillow (it saved my life!),
- ☑ Breastfeeding record chart to track baby's feeding and diapers (or just a notepad),
- ☑ A photo album or somewhere that you would want your baby's footprint to be recorded; nurses are happy to do it for you when you ask!,
- ☑ Healthy snacks for your support people or team,
- ☑ Camera (I love to use a Polaroid camera!) to record that amazing experience!

LEAVING EVERYTHING READY

When people start smiling at you at the grocery store for no reason and you feel like your catwalk is more like a penguin than a supermodel, you know it's almost time!! So start leaving everything ready. More important than having every detail of the nursery ready (which is what most of us may think) is having everything clean and newborn ready:

PACKING YOUR
HOSPITAL BAG

2 Nursing Bras

Comfortable Underwear

Dark colored socks

2 loose-fit outfits

Flip flops or comfortable shoes

Toiletries

Hairbands & Clips

Make up kit

Snacks

Water bottle + lime

HOME MADE CEREAL BAR

HOME MADE CEREAL BAR

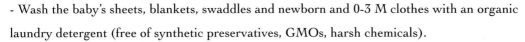

- Wash the baby's sheets, blankets, swaddles and newborn and 0-3 M clothes with an organic laundry detergent (free of synthetic preservatives, GMOs, harsh chemicals).
- Install your car seat.
- Set up the bassinet next to your bed.
- Get help to do a seriously deep clean of your home.
- Last but not least, treat yourself to a spa day. Do your nails, get a facial and wax everywhere!! Especially your bikini area.

ALMOST THERE !

By week 38 there are some methods that can help you to naturally induce labor:

- Stay active! Walk, walk and walk everywhere. Go to the park, walk your dogs, go up and down your stairs.
- Do 30 squats in the morning and 30 squats before bed (you can start doing this by week 35).
- Concentrate even more on your meditation and breathing techniques. Let your baby know that you are ready when he is, that everything is going to be fine, that mom and dad will take care of him and raise him to be a good human being.
- Stretch and do hip opening exercises every day.
- If you pass your due date you can try prenatal massages, acupuncture or acupressure. These are some labor-inducing techniques, some more invasive than the others, where certain pressure points are stimulated. Keep in mind these have to be practiced by a professional. Or just get a foot massage from your partner; that can also work!

II. HEALTHY eating

HEALTHY EATING

Eating healthy seems to be in every conversation between people today. This new magical product, or this new diet that really, really works: vegan, raw, paleo, OMG sooo overwhelming. We are constantly being bombarded by the media to consume this or that. But what really works? What option is the best for you and the one you can sustain in the long run? That answer can only be answered by YOU! Especially now that it is not only just about you anymore!

As the Institute of Integrative Nutrition teaches (the cool nutritional coaching school I attended), something every diet out there ignores is what they called "Bio-individuality," meaning that every person is completely different with different needs. We are bio-individuals, so things such as genes, age, sex, what you grew up eating, level of activity, etc., will determine what type of nutrition works best for you. Therefore, there is NO one size fits all diet, and what works for you may not work for me! So going back to the question: How do I know what works for me? The answer is very simple, yet complex: LEARN HOW TO CONNECT AND LISTEN TO YOUR BODY. Nowadays we are so worried about being connected. We are always trying to connect with everyone through Facebook, Instagram, Snap-chat, through this and that, but we completely forget and take for granted how important it is to actually connect with our body. So just do it! Pay attention to your mood, your energy level, your digestion, and your skin, after eating this or that. In that way you will find the right balance for you. (I know during pregnancy our body feels a little bit more unpredictable, but you can still listen to it!)

To tell you a little bit of my story, I grew up in a house where my mom gave us fruit juices with no added sugar, where sodas and chips were only for visitors and she cooked our lunch box food every morning. During my teens, especially my late teens, I wanted to be so skinny, I ate everything with a low-calorie, fat-free label. I pretty much bought everything advertised as low-calorie, not minding the crappy ingredient list (I'm expanding on this topic in the "Reading Food Labels & Shopping Tips" section). Then I experimented with veganism, which means not eating anything coming from animals (I got really sick and found out that as bad as I felt for animals, it wasn't a sustainable diet for my body). After that I added eggs and fish to my diet which made me feel so much better. That was my diet for a couple of years until I immersed myself more into the world of nutrition. I started listening to my body by adding certain foods in moderation (real food, not processed), looking for that balance, and I've never been healthier and felt better!! (Thinking it through, it's no wonder there was a spark of life in my belly at that time! I had never felt in better health! And it was then that the universe gave me the gift of being a mother.)

So erase the word diet from your head, especially now that you need the real deal for your baby to grow!! You need to eat real food and see how your body feels! I say moderation is the key. They say cheese is bad for you, ok, but if you tolerate it, you can eat it, but in moderation! Your body needs a little bit of everything (by everything I don't mean a little bit of donuts, cake, fries, etc.; I mean good carbs, fruits, veggies, real and quality meats, dairy and fats! The "Mommy-To-Be Pantry Lists" section will be your guide!).

Sooo the purpose of all that mumbo jumbo, from the beginning of this chapter until this point, was to explain why everything that follows related to food will be based on a TRADITIONAL DIET. This diet includes all foods in moderation, but only the highest and cleanest versions are used. In other words, we want to try going back to basics and eat just like our grandparents ate. Whole foods, minimum packaged or prepared, going for quality, nutrient dense foods!! So first let's have the following things in mind:

I recommend starting every day with a super tall glass of room temperature water (I drink the whole BPA-free bottle that is sitting on my night table from the night before!). It's good for your body to be awakened by water close to its temperature, on an empty stomach. This hydrates your organs and sets a healthy start to your body. Benefits will go sky-high just by adding some lime juice! This will help your body alkalize, meaning to maintain an optimal PH for normal operation in your cells (I'll talk a little more about this in a few pages!), help your digestion, your skin, your energy levels and believe it or not, your acidity problems when your belly is about to explode! Just remember not to brush your teeth immediately as this can affect your teeth enamel. (If you feel lime juice is too strong add some apple cider vinegar! It works just great!!)

 Love your greens with all your heart! They will keep you young, beautiful and healthy! Eat veggies every day of your life (no matter if you are pregnant or not), include them in all your meals if possible (especially leafy greens!). Try always to have raw and cooked veggies on your plate!

 Eat a rainbow and you will feel like a rainbow!! Keep your plate always colorful; that is always a good sign you are on the right track, color means life!

 Quality is better than quantity. No further explanation needed.

 Good fats are your new best friends; make peace with fats. That fat-free boom that the food industry drilled into our heads is not true at all. We need fats! (Especially your big belly! And specifically in your last trimester.) Of course we need the right ones, for our brains to work properly! Just because we can't see our brain (like we can see our thighs fattening) doesn't mean we don't have to take care of it! Let's start now; the brain is mainly made up of fat so it needs fats to be healthy! Fats are also important for our metabolism; they help us digest vitamins and minerals and they carry important fertility nutrients (Vitamin A). Plus they are the ones in charge of telling our brains we are full! Remember moderation is key, and stick to natural sources: coconut oil, butter, ghee (clarified butter: the milk protein, carbohydrates and water have been removed), red palm oil, olive oil, natural fats from animal protein!

Our real archenemy is processed sugar. Avoid added sugar in your foods at all cost; it is hidden every-where with different names, from your prepackaged pasta sauce to your cereal. Get sugar from natural sources like fruits and vegetables such as carrots, sweet potatoes and beets. If you want to use extra go for natural sweeteners like maple syrup, honey, coconut palm sugar, dates.

 Control your portion sizes especially when eating animal protein (but remember you still need lots of pro-tein for your little one!!). In the USA people eat almost 4 times the portion size our bodies' need, which ends up in inflammation and disease such as heart disease, especially when bad quality proteins (fed with GMO grains and full of antibiotics) are consumed.

 If you tolerate dairy eat it moderately almost as a garnish, a little cheese here and there! (Also give goat and sheep cheeses a try! I love them! You can also try milk and yogurt version of both!)

 Add a protein, a good fat and a complex carb (quinoa, sweet potato, brown rice, etc.) to every meal to control your blood sugar levels!

 Give yourself time every meal to really ENJOY your food! Do not eat in front of the TV, computers or with your eyes on your phone. Chew your food thoroughly and focus on the yummy smell, texture and appear-ance of it! This will make meal time even more special; you won't overeat and you'll get all the enzymes and energy from your food! (I love thinking on all the good the food I eat is doing for my body. I almost imagine my organs and cells doing a happy dance; this makes me crave more and more nutrient-dense fuel!)

Without further ado:

FERTILITY DIET

Yes! What you are giving your body in terms of food and lifestyle can affect your fertility (for moms and dads to be too!). It is no wonder that your reproductive system will be in better shape to plant a seed when given quality nutrients for this to happen. Start cleaning out your body first before trying to get pregnant. Hint: Sperm takes 74 days to mature, so just make it a lifestyle.

In a nutshell your fertility diet needs to be rich in these vitamins and nutrients:

Vitamin A (makes estrogen): Butter, eggs, liver, red palm oil, carrots and sweet potatoes, kale, spinach, collard greens and butternut squash, among others.

Vitamin D (makes sex hormones): Cod liver oil, milk, pork, seafood, mushrooms, egg yolks and sun, among others.

Vitamin K2 (works together with vitamin A and D, sperm depends on it): Butter, shellfish, organ meats and eggs, among others.

Vitamin E (sperm maturity): Olive oil, avocados, almonds, spinach, asparagus, beet greens, whole grains, red palm oil, leafy greens, hazelnuts and sunflower seeds, among others.

Vitamins B, B12, B6, Folate (make sex hormones, balance estrogen and progesterone, make DNA for new cells): Milk, leafy greens, banana, meat, yogurt, fish, eggs, egg yolks, whole grains, liver, fish, poultry, clams and lentils, among others.

Zinc (maintains a healthy thyroid, makes eggs and sex hormones): Oysters, liver, fish, crab, shrimp, spinach, pumpkin seeds, flax seeds, beef, mushrooms and beans, among others.

STEP 1

Ditch sugars and simple and refined carbohydrates. These affect insulin in the blood which ends up causing an imbalance in the hormones needed for reproduction.

NO to sodas, white bread, processed muffins, cakes, candy, etc.

yes! to brown rice, quinoa, ancient grains, whole grains, legumes and natural sweeteners in controlled amounts (maple syrup, honey, dates).

STEP 2

Ditch saturated and trans fats. They decrease insulin sensitivity, which causes the body to absorb sugar more rapidly, and causes inflammation which ends up in ovulatory infertility. Remember portion control is key. Healthy fats help absorb antioxidants from foods and carry fertility nutrients.

NO to artificial fats such as margarine, corn oil, soybean oil, shortening present in processed baked goods, commercially fried food and fat-free products.

yes! to traditional full fats, grass-fed butter, milk, cheese and yogurt, ghee, olive oil, coconut oil and fats from animal protein, especially cod liver oil.

STEP 3

Go for quality animal proteins (grass-fed or pastured) which provide vitamins necessary for conception to take place. Seafood is an essential source of DHA and omega-3. Remember portion control is key, and don't forget your plant protein sources too! (Beans, lentils, nuts & seeds).

Vitamin A (egg yolks and grass-fed meat)
Vitamin D (seafood, pork and grass-fed meat)
Zinc (oysters, grass-fed meat and seafood)
Iron (grass-fed meat and chicken)

STEP 4

Get your greens from ecological fruits and vegetables. Focus on produce rich in folate (natural form of folic acid) which you can see in the "Mommy-To-Be Pantry Lists" section.

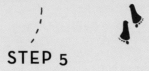

STEP 5

Stay active and follow a healthy lifestyle. Start by relaxing with things like yoga, breathing techniques and meditation (conception rates go up when women are relaxed. Also stress can reduce sperm count!! So just breathe!).
Also bring your heart rate up by going for a run, to the gym, engaging in sports clubs, motivating each other; you are in this together and that's the only way you are going to be successful, from conception to parenthood! Try lowering alcohol consumption and please quit smoking NOW!

Trimester by Trimesters
NUTRITIONAL NEEDS

If you followed the fertility diet congrats! You are excellently on track. As I have mentioned throughout the book, nutrition is not only crucial for your baby's health from conception to birth and later development overall, but I can also reassure you this makes the difference between a healthy, fun, and enjoyable pregnancy and a really nasty one! From weight gain, mood swings, energy levels to pain and aches control!

As a super mommy-to-be, you need to concentrate on nutrient-dense foods, quality foods, closer to their natural state, meaning no processed foods full of preservatives and additives.

Pregnancy nutrition is a continuation of the fertility diet of course; you need to concentrate on quality whole grains, vegetables (great source of folic acid, iron and fiber), good fats, quality proteins especially those rich in the vitamins and minerals mentioned!

To recap and expand a little more we are looking to include as many of these nutrients as possible:

Iron: Grass-fed meat, chicken, spirulina, veggies (especially kale, broccoli, asparagus, beets, collard greens), nuts and dried apricots, among others.

Folate: Beans, dark leafy greens and cashews, among others.

DHA, good fats and omega-3: Cod liver oil, fish, grass-fed meat, butter and ghee, among others.

Vitamin A: Cod liver oil, egg yolks and grass-fed meat, sweet potatoes, carrots, dark leafy greens and mangos, among others.

Vitamin D: Seafood, pork, grass-fed meat, cod liver oil, egg yolks and, among other things, some sun!!

Zinc: Shellfish, lamb, red meat, lentils, chickpeas, pumpkin and quinoa, among others.

Iodine: Himalayan pink salt, kosher salt or sea salt.

Polyunsaturated fats: Wild fish and shellfish, among others.

Calcium: Quality dairy, fermented dairy, dark leafy greens, nuts and broths (especially bone broths), among others.

Maybe you will find this a little overwhelming because you can get bombarded by a thousand opinions and diets recommending you should eat this amount of proteins, this amount of fats...so my advice is simple, stick to real foods, the ones we've been talking about throughout the book! That is key! And as the awesome Nina Planck, author of the book *Real Food for Mother and Baby*, recommends, in addition to real, traditional, quality foods focus on the following layout for what foods you need to emphasize each trimester: in the first trimester you don't need to eat "for two," you just need micronutrients (vitamins) for your baby's parts to form. In the second trimester focus on calcium and proteins to support your baby's bone and muscle build up. And finally in the last trimester eat plenty of fish and good fats for your baby's brain! That simple!

And because I know for lots of us (including me some years ago), calories and lbs. are still soo important (now we need to care about nutrients!!!), I will go to the million dollar question: How much is a healthy weight gain? According to the American Pregnancy Association, if you have a healthy starting weight, it is healthy to gain between 25-35 lbs. or 10-15 kg. If you are underweight: 28-40 lbs. or 12-18 kg, and if you are overweight you will also need to gain some weight: 15-25 lbs. or 6-11 kg. The normal pattern is to gain 2-4 lbs. or 1-2 kg the first trimester and then approximately 1 lb. or 0.5 kg per week for the rest of the pregnancy. This is not carved in stone! I had a healthy starting weight and only gained 18 lbs. or 8 kg in total and I was as healthy as a raw crispy yummy kale leaf! (Actually my doctor told me that as I started with a healthy weight, I shouldn't worry about the weight gain; it was perfectly healthy to gain less than what is standard. The main focus should be on eating well and getting those lbs. or kg from real food!! Because you really do need those extra calories for protein to reach your baby! So consult your doctor if you need further information about the topic!)

First

TRIMESTER

0 Extra Calories Needed Daily

Your baby is still a tiny embryo. You don't need lots of foods; you just need to focus on quality calories, micronutrients (vitamins) and lots of liquids. As this is the period where most of us experience morning sickness and nausea (which can occur at any time during the day!), you want to take it slowly with your stomach but still get the vitamins and nutrients needed for these crucial weeks where the embryo is developing and the nervous system, heart, eyes, ears, limbs and brain are forming. The use of unrefined salt such as Himalayan pink salt, sea salt and kosher salt are crucial for building up the body supply that starts picking up.

During my first trimester I survived on green juices, smoothies and gallons of soup, homemade of course, with real ingredients. Bone broths, seafood and fish stocks are great sources of nutrients during this period.

Second

TRIMESTER

Around 300 Extra Calories Needed Daily

(1 cup Greek yogurt + ¼ cup almonds)

During this period the bones and muscles of your baby are being formed, that's why by around week 27 you can start feeling some boxing action from your little one! That being said, this trimester you need to focus on calcium (for the skeleton) and protein (for muscles).

You will think calcium=milk, protein=meat, but you need to take into account that your growing uterus will slow down your digestion so try experimenting with different sources which feel better for you (and for those who do not tolerate dairy that well too). Get your calcium from quality grass-fed dairy products such as cottage cheese and kefir which are easier to digest (plus fermented dairy has more available calcium!!). Also remember that calcium needs fats to be properly absorbed, so take advantage of that real whole milk, real sour cream and yummy, real cheeses! There are also excellent dairy-free sources such as sesame seeds, sardines, amaranth, chard, kale, almonds, parsley, beans, salmon, chickpeas… check out this complete list:

Foods in Regular Portion Size	Miligrams (Mg)
Plain yogurt (8 oz/220g)	415
Figs (1 cup)	300
Sardines (3 oz/85g)	347
Whole milk (1 cup)	276
Amaranth (1 cup)	270
Collard Greens (1 cup)	266
Spinach (1 cup)	245
Hard cheeses (1 oz/28g)	222
Mozzarella Cheese (1 oz/28g)	200
Kale (2 cups)	200
Turnip greens (1 cup)	198
Salmon (3 ounces/85g)	181
Bok choy (1 cup)	158
Cottage cheese (1 cup)	145
Feta cheese (1 oz/28g)	140
Sesame seeds (2 T)	128
Tahini/ sesame seeds paste (2 T)	130
Almonds (1oz/28g)	70
Sesame Seeds (1 T)	64
Dill, Basil, Oregano, Thyme (2 t)	54-64
Sunflower seeds (1 oz/28g)	50
Celery (1 cup)	48
Broccoli (1 cup)	48
Cauliflower (1 cup)	42
Brussels sprouts (1 cup)	40
Asparagus (1 cup)	32
Lettuce (2 cups)	31

Protein, in addition to supporting baby's muscles, helps prevent swelling and premature birth! So let's step it up! For protein you can try eggs, chicken, and grass-fed meat but also legumes such as beans and lentils. Just make sure to soak them overnight to make them smoother on the stomach (we don't like that heaviness feeling and surely our partners prefer no gas!). Nuts and seeds are great too (think peanut butter goodies and homemade trail mix for snacks yum!).

Third

TRIMESTER

Around 400 Extra calories Needed Daily

(1 cup Greek yogurt + ¼ cup almonds + 1 banana)

In this last trimester your baby is really growing in size, especially his little brain. As we all want little Einsteins at home try to focus this period on good sources of fat. As you know, the brain is mainly made up of fat! Go for clean foods with healthy fats. Get your omega-6s and omega-3s from lean meats, cod liver oil, eggs, nuts, seeds, ghee, coconut oil, grass-fed butter, seafood and fish. Note that the calorie need is higher now; so again, don't waste your intake with empty calories but with real ones! Try eating smaller portions of foods and quality snacks throughout the day. This will really help you ease problems with your now totally compressed digestive system, especially that annoying heartburn. You are almost there! Just feel how exciting it is to know that your baby's weight has tripled by now! And all through nutritious, healthy and quality foods you have given him! You are such a great momma.

Fourth
TRIMESTER

AKA Breast Feeding Months ←

Around 300 Extra calories Needed Daily

(1 cup Greek yogurt + 1 banana + 1 T chia seeds)

I hope you are planning on breastfeeding; in my opinion it is the best first gift you can give to your little one. Through your milk you will transfer immune cells and antibodies to protect your baby against infection and allergies (meaning natural vaccines, from your own body!! Just how cool are our bodies!?!). You will also see that it is sooo much more convenient just to take your booby out in the middle of the night than preparing formula bottles. Besides, what I loved the most is the connection and bond that is created with your baby. If you are still not convinced I need to tell you breastfeeding will make you naturally shrink your uterus postpartum and easily get rid of extra pounds!!

During your breastfeeding months continue the protein and fat consumption you were taking during pregnancy and also keep taking your prenatal vitamins. The first three months of life are known as the "Fourth Trimester." Here your baby's brain is still in need of some good, real fats! Especially DHA which can be obtained from fish and cod liver oil. You need lots and lots of fluids to get that milk production on point! Get them from water, coconut milk, coconut water, chicken soup and broths. Have in mind you need to limit your alcohol and caffeine consumption because they are transferred through your milk (trans fats are also transferred to your baby so please continue with your real food priority mindset!!!). You can have a drink if you are not going to be breastfeeding in the next two hours, and remember too much caffeine can affect your baby's sleep (you for sure don't need more of that!).

Enjoy your breastfeeding months; they can sometimes be difficult but it is totally worth it. For me, it was a great time! (I strongly recommend taking a breastfeeding class or having the support of a lactation consultant!! Latching is not as primal and instinctive as one might think, you actually need some technique!) Extend it until you feel like it. It's really your decision; it will never be bad for your baby, your milk is so perfect and nutrient-complete that it is never enough for your baby. The American Academy of Pediatrics recommends breastfeeding for at least 6 months.

Goji Berries

HEMP SEEDS

SUPER FOODS

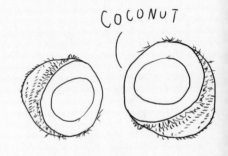
COCONUT

CACAO SEEDS

FOR SUPER Moms!

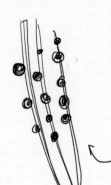
ACAI BERRY

SPIRULINA

CHIA seeds

SUPERFOODS FOR SUPERMOMMAS

What are superfoods? These are foods with the highest content of phytonutrients. They are the most nutritionally dense foods available. In simpler terms, they actually act as superheroes by providing lots and lots of nutrients that fight all sources of diseases, for a low-calorie quota! From improving overall health by cleansing and alkalizing your body (for those who don't know, we always want our bodies to be less acidic, meaning towards an alkaline PH level of 7.0. Disease cells are produced in an acidic environment.), to supplying the mineral and vitamin quota needed. I treat superfoods as my multivitamin pills; you can't get enough of them, so be sneaky like me and start adding them to your daily meals everywhere! In the "Recipes" section I'll give you ideas!

These are some of my favorite superfoods that will make you a supermomma!

 ## GOJI BERRIES

Also known as wolfberry, these tiny berries are a complete protein source, full of amino acids, trace minerals (zinc, iron, copper, and calcium among others) and vitamins B1, B2, B6 and vitamin E. They are rich in polysaccharides, beta-carotene and mineral germanium that fortify the immune system (during pregnancy your body is working full load! So the immune system gets weakened, which could easily lead to infections and flu). Goji berries also promote longevity and healthy hormones, improve vision and support neurological and cardiovascular health. They are great antioxidants and can also enhance your libido and sexual life! (Very handy if you are following the fertility diet or you are practicing making a child!!)

I usually buy dried organic goji berries, but you can also find them in different forms (extract powder, juice or freshly picked!). I use goji berries as toppings in salads, bowls, homemade trail mix and on top of my avocado toast.

HEMP SEEDS

Hemp seeds come from a plant used to make anything made of cotton, timber or petroleum. For those of you wondering, hemp and marijuana are both classified as cannabis sativa but consuming hemp seeds won't make you or your baby high. They will give you a high in protein, essential fatty acids and immune system support. Hemp seeds are another favorite on my list for being a complete source of protein. They contain over twenty trace minerals, all the essential amino acids and high contents of fatty acids. These nutty flavor seeds are around 35% pure digestible protein, one of the richest and purest forms of protein (only spirulina exceeds hemp seeds in protein). Perfect for your little one's brain development, these seeds are around 47% good fats, omega-3s and omega-6s. In addition they are rich in vitamin E and fiber and other minerals for mommies-to-be such as iron, calcium and zinc.

I buy raw shelled hemp seeds and hemp seed oil. Also, when the ingredient list is favorable I buy hemp seed protein. I love these seeds for making milk, it is the easiest. I also add them to smoothies, drinks, bowls, salads, etc.

Spirulina

Spirulina is my favorite superfood ever!!! I do really sneak it everywhere I can!! It is an ancient sweet water alga. It is rich in chlorophyll, protein, vitamins, trace minerals and anti-oxidants (3-4 times more than berries). What is almost impossible for some to believe is that this alga is a complete source of protein containing all essential amino acids. It is actually the highest concentrated protein known (by weight). It supports muscle, strength, endurance, blood sugar, neurological health, strong bones, as well as balances brain chemistry. In addition, and what I really love and consider a real superpower, is that it helps clean your body from artificial chemicals, pesticides and radioactive materials (which we are constantly exposed to even when eating organic). Great for mommies-to-be, this superfood contains as much iron as red meat! It's an incredible immune system booster, rich in vitamins A, B1, B2

B6, E, K. OMG and I could continue for ages talking about spirulina.

You may have heard that spirulina may not be safe during pregnancy due to contamination. There have not been any reported cases, but just to be extra sure and to be able to get all the awesomeness from it, buy from a trusted source. Look for certified organic spirulina, a pure strain grown in an unpolluted environment. Consult your doctor if you want to be extra sure.

I buy powdered organic spirulina grown in a biosecure zone (read labels!) and literally use it everywhere: I use 1 t in my salad dressings, smoothies and drinks, in my homemade granola and oatmeal, swirled into my yogurt or in my water bottle.

CACAO

I know what you are thinking, maybe you have read that during pregnancy one should lower chocolate consumption to a minimum, but here I'm not talking about commercial chocolate but cacao the seed! Only one ingredient from the commercial chocolate ingredient list (no sugar, no dairy, no chemicals, just the cacao). Cacao is considered one of the top 10 superfoods because it's a natural source for iron, zinc, vitamin C, omega-6 fatty acids, and soluble fiber - all nutrients needed during pregnancy (go back to the "Trimester by Trimester Nutritional Needs" section and confirm for yourself!). Serotonin is also present in cacao which helps you stay calm and relax (I bet you need this during these months). Cacao is also rich in antioxidants, magnesium and copper, among other amazing properties!

I buy raw cacao in the form of nibs, powder and butter. The powder I use in baked goods, smoothies and drinks, and the nibs are one of my favorite toppings for bowls and yogurts, among others.

Maca

Maca is a root cultivated centuries ago in South America. Like goji berries maca supports the hormonal and nervous systems, as well as the cardiovascular system and musculature. But it is well known for increasing energy (something very helpful during your first trimester where you feel constantly drained), endurance and libido, and can also help you improve your mood by increasing your blood oxygen content. It also supports the endocrine system, the adrenal and thyroid.

There is a little chitchatting about consuming maca during pregnancy because it is considered an herbal supplement, and manufacturers, to be protected from potential liability, caution consumers. The truth is that it has been consumed for thousands of years by civilizations without problems or side effects, and there are still no reported cases of complications. Still if you want to be extra sure, consult your doctor before taking. But you need to know maca is incredibly good for you and it also helps you during breastfeeding!

I usually buy organic powdered maca root and add 1 to 2 t to smoothies, drinks, baked goods and anything with chocolate; it pairs so nicely!

Bee honey & Pollen

Not simply honey and pollen but all bee products are considered incredibly nutrient-dense. Honey is a very digestible, natural and raw form of sugar. When consumed organically, raw and unfiltered, it fills the body with probiotics, antioxidants, enzymes and minerals. Honey has lots of medicinal benefits due to its antibacterial and moisture-retaining properties. This is of great help when you are feeling under the weather while preggo. It's an excellent alternative to OTC medicine for flu. Remember to always try to look for natural remedies that keep your little one safe!

Bee pollen is considered one of the most complete foods in the world. It contains eighteen vitamins, almost all B, C, D and E, carotenes and essential amino acids. It is almost 25% protein, containing protein that is five to seven times easier to assimilate (because it's in a predigested form) than eggs, cheese or meat. Bee pollen is also rich in minerals needed by moms-to-be like calcium, iron, zinc and sodium. The antioxidant levels are incredibly high, increasing longevity and rejuvenating sexual organs. It also increases strength, energy and speed as well as promoting muscle growth and definition. And also very handy for us, pollen contains eleven different amino acids that aid digestion, perfect when feeling constipated.

I buy raw unfiltered honey, even better when it's wild, and dried bee pollen (stored in the freezer to maintain nutrients). I add honey to anything consumed raw where I need sweetness, because cooking honey will kill all the enzymes. Honey is also one of my main ingredients for a flu kick-ass drink (see "Recipe" section). I add both in smoothies, desserts or drinks.

 # Coconut

I love having coconut in its different forms from water to oil. It's another superhero! It improves the absorption of vitamins and amino acids; it's made up of 90% raw saturated fat which supports the immune system (great antibacterial, antifungal, antiviral), nervous system, thyroid gland and skin, and provides fast energy! (If you feel like coffee is the only thing that picks you up, have a T of coconut oil with water or your favorite drink!) Coconut also promotes healthy cholesterol, increases your metabolism and is a great antioxidant!! Coconut water hydrates your body with electrolytes, just what your body needs when active (no need for energy or sports drinks full of nasty things); it is also your best ally when breast feeding.

I buy unrefined, cold pressed coconut oil and I pretty much cook everything with it given that it won't lose its properties even at high temperatures. I use coconut cream as a spread or as butter in baked goods. I love buying wild coconuts that they cut open for you to drink, but when I'm not in a tropical location I look for raw coconut water in stores, never heated, not from concentrate and no extra ingredients added. Coconut water is a must in my smoothies! Coconut milk is my favorite ingredient to use for extra creaminess in pasta sauces or soups! Last but not least unsweetened coconut flakes are the kick to my homemade granola.

Golden Berries

Also known as Incan berries, these berries are rich in beta-carotene and vitamin C, and have anti-inflammatory, antiviral, and antioxidant properties. When eaten fresh the chewable seeds help your digestive system!! (Let's eat a handful instead of OTC laxatives!!)

I buy dried golden berries to add to my spoonable smoothies and homemade trail mix, or tossed in salads. I get really excited when I can find them fresh (not that easy, trust me). Just imagine my excitement every time I go to my country house in Colombia where I harvest them and eat them right away! I eat them like popcorn!! Sooo good!

CHIA SEEDS

Chia seeds are part of the three musketeers I use as toppings (chia, hemp, and flax seeds; I use whole flax seeds to get the jelly detoxing effect, and ground flax seeds to get the healthy fats!). Two tablespoons of these cute seeds have 4 grams of protein, 100 ml of calcium and 7.5 grams of dietary fiber that support the digestive tract. They are rich in minerals, antioxidants and omega-3 fatty acids; they actually have the highest omega-3 content of any plant food. When they enter the stomach they form a gel that helps clean your intestines and rehydrate you. And last but not least, this increase in size when turned into gel will make you feel more satisfied!

I buy organic chia seeds to add to my granola, salads, smoothies, bowls, fruit, etc. I love to soak them in milk or kefir to eat as a pudding, or in water to use as a substitute for eggs in recipes when a bonding agent is needed!!

Fermented Foods

We usually treat bacteria as the bad guys, but that's not always the case; we need trillions of bacteria in our digestive system to be healthy. Our intestines need enzymatic activity to help us process our food and get rid of all the toxins we eat (sadly, even more nowadays). Fermented foods then are the producers of these goodfellas bacteria; the ones responsible for providing better digestion, improving the immune system, detoxifying our intestines, and helping us better absorb the vitamins and nutrients in our food. An extra superpower of these foods is to prevent and fight candida (AKA yeast infection, women's all-time worst enemy). It is super important for us to consume fermented foods; we need to have healthy flora down there for our babies to be born in a healthy "environment" (for those who want to shoot for natural birth!).

I get my fermented food quota from the following:

Kimchi or sauerkraut (raw fermented vegetables)
Kefir and yogurt
Kombucha
Miso paste
Sourdough bread

Quinoa & Amaranth

Quinoa was a complete game changer from the first time it came into my life. I wanted to have it all the time! For breakfast (as a porridge), lunch and dinner!! Even in my sushi!! I was completely hooked! What I love about quinoa, besides its versatility and easiness to prepare, is how nutritionally complete it is. It is high in protein compared to other grains, contains all essential amino acids, has vitamins B6 and B2 and minerals mommies-to-be love such as folate, zinc, potassium, magnesium, and omega-3 fats. It's rich in fiber and helps clean the digestive tract! Plus it is gluten-free and so low in calories. Amaranth is very similar but not as popular as quinoa (it's not labeled as a superfood yet). It is high in protein too, and contains amino acids, folate, calcium, magnesium, iron and vitamins such as A, C, B5, B6 and folate. It raises energy levels, controls hormones and acts as an antioxidant.

I buy organic quinoa and in the mornings cook it as a porridge with milk; also, anywhere rice goes I tend to substitute quinoa. I also love to pop it and add it to my yogurt, granola, salads and my yummy Raw Superfoods Balls, you will see ahead. I also buy organic amaranth and use in very similar ways to quinoa!

Dried Goji Berries   Cacao Nibs   Dried Golden Berries

organics

TO BUY or NOT TO BUY

I know buying organic is expensive (tell my hubby about it), and that's pretty much everyone's excuse for not buying organic, but make an effort; your body will pay you back with better health! (Just think - less money spent on doctors and medicine in the near future!) That's why I use The Dirty Dozen™ and The Clean Fifteen™ produce lists to guide myself on what is perfectly ok to buy conventional or what, no matter what, I will buy organic. For the updated lists every year check out www.ewg.org.

In the long run, it's not only because of the pesticides and chemicals found in conventional products that we should buy organic (these pesticides can cause thyroid dysfunction, cancer, kidney disease and birth defects. OMG a little scary…), but for the fact that an organic vegetable or fruit is more nutrient-dense than a conventional one. So if you buy conventional blueberries, you are not only eating all the chemicals, but you will also need to eat larger amounts of the product to get the same nutrients and vitamins that you get from organic versions. Which translates to higher costs, so just try going for the organic option!

The DIRTY 12™

1. Strawberries
2. Apples
3. Nectarines
4. Peaches
5. Celery
6. Grapes
7. Cherries
8. Spinach
9. Tomatoes
10. Bell peppers
11. Cherry tomatoes
12. Cucumbers
+ Hot peppers
+ Kale / Collard greens

CLEAN 15™

1. Avocado
2. Sweet corn*
3. Pineapples
4. Cabbage
5. Sweet peas (frozen)
6. Onions
7. Asparagus
8. Mangoes
9. Papayas*
10. Kiwi
11. Eggplant
12. Honeydew
13. Grapefruit
14. Cantaloup
15. Cauliflower

Follow our
EXTRA
GOODIES
link to
download!
WWW.FFTHMIAMI.COM/
EXTRA-GOODIES

* A small amount of sweet corn, papaya and summer squash sold in the United States is produced from genetically engineered seed stock (GE). Buy organic varieties of these crops if you want to avoid GE produce. GE/GM/GMOs are foods with genes that have been artificially altered to make them more resistant to pesticides and chemicals. Sadly, eating these unknown modified organisms in our foods is linked to cancer and infertility, among other diseases.

USEFUL CLEANING TIP

Before cooking or eating a fruit or vegetable (especially if it's eaten raw), wash and clean the produce. Some options are using warm water and then cleaning with a cloth. For my berries, even if they are organic I wash them with water and a hint of vinegar or lemon and baking soda. I leave the fruit in a bowl with the solution for a minute, and then rinse off with tap water. Remember that even when a product is labeled organic it may still contain harmful ingredients, but in lower quantities than conventional produce (which is still better in the long run!).

$$$ TIP:

Look for more affordable prices in farmer's markets and farms around your area! This is also great for buying quality animal protein, dairy and fresh produce. You can get to
 know your farmers and their practices!

READING FOOD LABELS
& SHOPPING TIPS

You need to become a label detective, no matter how crazy everyone around you may think you are (a great habit learnt from the inspiring Vani Hari AKA the Food Babe). We don't want to eat crap! So we need to start doing something about it. The food industry bombards us with misleading labels all day long. Open your eyes, follow these tips and make smart decisions when going through the supermarket aisles.

Usually people do read product labels but only the nutrition facts area, mainly for the number of calories and that's it. We need to change that mindset created by the food industry. It's not the number of calories that matter; it is the quality of those that counts!

Quick example: It's not the same to have 100 calories of Oreo cookies versus 100 calories in one tablespoon of peanut butter (bought organic, containing no extra oils or sweeteners). The 100 calories of Oreo cookies are composed of: unbleached enriched flour, (wheat flour, niacin, reduced iron, thiamine mononitrate {vitamin B1}, riboflavin {vitamin B2}, folic acid {vitamin B9}), sugar, palm and/or canola oil, cocoa (processed with alkali), high fructose corn syrup, leavening (baking soda and/or calcium phosphate), cornstarch, salt, soy lecithin, vanillin - an artificial flavor, and chocolate. The 100 calories in a tablespoon of peanut butter contains healthy fats and protein from the ground peanuts; one real ingredient VS thousands of artificial ones.

So let's start reading the INGREDIENT LISTS too!

SHOPPING TIPS

BUYING VEGGIES & FRUITS

As I mentioned earlier, I always use The Dirty Dozen™ and The Clean Fifteen™ lists to see what to buy organic or conventional. When buying produce it is handy to read the codes on the produce stickers:

🍎 Conventionally grown are 4 digit codes starting with 3 or 4.

🍎 Organic are 5 digit codes starting with 9.

🍎 Genetically modified are 5 digit codes starting with 8.

I also love buying frozen organic fruits for my smoothies and some veggies for soups. Despite what everyone thinks, frozen produce keeps its nutrients. In fact frozen produce can sometimes be more nutrient-dense than fresh because it is picked when perfectly ripe and flash frozen to keep the nutrients. Also, in all the time that passes from harvesting until it reaches stores, the produce is exposed to different temperatures, light and movement that make it lose some nutrients. So frozen fruit for me is a great option! Plus it gives my smoothies an awesome texture I love!

BUYING PACKAGED PRODUCTS

It is always a good sign to see your fridge full of bright colors from veggies and fruits instead of packaged goods. Try to reduce your packaged goods consumption to the really essential products. Remember that for products to be preserved a long time while being packaged, not-so-good ingredients are usually used. So my general take on this is to:

1. Look for the Certified Organic and Non-GMO label.

2. Go for products with the lowest number of ingredients (no extra sugars or nasty oils added).

3. Put back any product containing ingredients that you can't pronounce or are part of the following list even if the product is certified organic!! These ingredients literally kill you slowly:

✗ **High Fructose Corn syrup** (impacts the hormones insulin and leptin, promoting fat storage and uncontrollable appetite. Also causes tissue damage);

✗ **Monosodium Glutamate** (MSG) also commonly known as **Yeast extract, any "hydro-lyzed protein", any "hydrolyzed", ending in "glutamate"** (makes food taste amazing, of course used in junk food. Causes obesity and if you are allergic to it, which is very common and rarely known, will cause vomiting, headaches and depression, among others; also linked with hyperactivity in children);

✗ Preservatives: **BHA, BHT, Propylene Glycol, Nitrates, Sodium Nitrate, Propyl Gallate** (linked to Alzheimer's disease, cancer, central nervous system depression and kidney damage);

✗ **"Partially hydrogenated"** = Trans fat {**Cottonseed oil, Soy oil, Sunflower oil, Safflower oil, Margarine**} (raises risks of heart disease, raises blood sugar, creates more and bigger fat cells, and affects your immune system);

✗ **Artificial and Natural flavors.** Can be anything from animal parts and powdered rocks to petroleum. They are everything but natural (linked to Alzheimer's and Parkinson's diseases, depression, strokes, migraines, obesity, fatigue, and an irresistible desire to eat more and more);

✗ Food Dyes: **Yellow #5, Yellow #6, Red #2, Red #3, Red #40, Blue #1, Blue #2, Caramel coloring.** Made up of petroleum and insect parts (the accumulation of eating them throughout your life raises risks of cancer);

X **Refined, enriched, bleached, and white flour.** In these flours all grain minerals and vitamins are destroyed. In addition chlorine and more chemicals are used to bleach them and obtain the white color. (They cause your pancreatic enzymes to overwork, permanent inflammation, and make you addicted to them!! This leads to obesity and glycemic problems);

X **Dough Conditioners: Potassium Bromate, Azodicarbonamide, DATEM.** They are found in shelved bread and are created from GMOs and synthetic ingredients. A tip is to buy from a trusted bakery or buy frozen sprouted grain breads (linked to allergy, asthma and hormonal imbalance);

X **Carrageenan** Used mainly in dairy products and nut milks as emulsifier (causes stomach issues, inflammation and problems from irritable bowel syndrome to colon cancer);

X **Aspartame, Saccharin, Neotame, Sucralose, Erythritol, Acesulfame Potassium, Acesulfame K.** Commercial names: Splenda, NutraSweet, Sweet'N Low (slow down your metabolism and make you crave more sugar!!);

X AVOID ADDED SUGARS: **Barley malt, Beet sugar, Brown sugar, Buttered syrup, Caramel, Carob syrup, Corn syrup, Dextran, Dextrose, Diastatic malt, Ethyl maltol, Fructose, Glucose, Glucose solids, Invert sugar, Lactose, Malt syrup, Maltodextrin, Maltose, Maltitol, Raw sugar, Refiner's syrup, Sorbitol, Sorghum Syrup, Sucrose, Turbinado sugar, Yellow sugar.** (increase your blood sugar triggering irritability and depression. Make your skin wrinkled by disrupting collagen and elastin, destroy your immune system, cause cardiovascular disease, lead to cancer, and what is worst is that they make you sooo addicted, they react in our brains just like drugs!).

BUYING ANIMAL PROTEINS

When buying animal proteins in the supermarket I look for the following labels: organic (no antibiotics or hormones used), free-range or cage-free (animals can move freely), pastured, grass-fed or pastured raised (animals have access to green areas and are fed with grass rather than grains), and certified humane (better treatment of animals). In my humble opinion it's better to eat more plant protein than have poor quality animal protein (especially chicken, beef and pork). You can save your body from eating a lot of GMOs, antibiotics, and stress hormones released by animals raised in factory farming!

I buy:
- Organic, grass-fed beef
- Organic chicken
- Organic turkey
- Nitrate-free organic turkey bacon
- Wild salmon
- Wild, locally caught fish and shrimp
- Organic, Pastured eggs (***happy chickens raised outdoors!)

BUYING DAIRY

For me it is a must to buy all organic dairy products (I'm truly scared of consuming regular dairy products, more for us living in the US). Regular, non-organic milk is full of antibiotics (because it is impossible for the massive milk industry to control diseases and these antibiotics kill the good bacteria in our guts! Remember probiotics? They help us absorb nutrients!). Plus the industry also feeds cows with GMO grains, like corn and soy, and provides growth hormone (rBGH) to boost milk production.

When buying milk, no matter if you are pregnant or not, you should buy WHOLE organic grass-fed (yes! not fat-free or 2%, but whole). Organic milk comes from grass-fed cows not treated with growth hormones or antibiotics. This milk is actually higher in antioxidants and vitamins compared to regular milk. It is also richer in CLA (good fat), beta-carotene vitamin E and omega-3. But the downside of organic milk is that most of that sold in supermarkets is pasteurized and homogenized. Should we consider raw milk then?

I know you have probably heard that pregnant women should avoid unpasteurized milk at all costs for the risk of bacteria. But if you can really find a trustworthy source for raw milk, like a local provider, please don't deprive yourself of the benefits of drinking real milk!! (Lots of real vitamin A and D that we need!!)

The FDA usually scares us, preggos especially, about the risks of drinking raw milk, but in fact the risks are lower than when eating raw veggies or deli meats. (Actually, in a study done in 2003 by the FDA they found out that there were 500 more cases of listeria disease caused by deli meats than by raw milk).

Milk pasteurization (the process done to prevent bacteria in milk that has to be kept for days in a fridge before being consumed) kills the good and the bad including folic acid and vitamins A, B6 and C. This process also deactivates enzymes and damages omega-3 fats and milk protein. The resulting product is a lower calcium- and overall nutrient-deficient milk. Especially when you see the ultra-high temperature pasteurization label (UHT); AKA pasteurization on steroids, the end result will be a milk lacking nutrients that when consumed causes calcium deficiency, inflammation and cancer (OMG this is real!!!).

To sum up this milky situation, if you can have access to a truly trustable source of raw milk go for it!!! (It is so difficult to find, even illegal in some states in the US.) If not, please, please buy whole organic from grass-fed cows! (Try to find milk that is only pasteurized rather than ultra-pasteurized!)

> I buy:
> - Milk (organic & grass-fed cows),
> - Organic and grass-fed kefir & yogurt (no extra sugar added),
> - Goat milk yogurt,
> - Organic and grass-fed cheeses (avoid soft cheeses and queso fresco),
> - Organic and grass-fed goat and sheep cheeses,
> - Imported cheeses with the protected designation of origin (PDO) logo, so you know it really comes from Europe or wherever it's from. (Their cows are healthier than our cows!)

BUYING OIL

DO NOT BUY sunflower oil, canola oil, cottonseed oil, or margarine (they are full of GMOs and the process from which they are obtained is really bad for our health!! Trust me).

Go for:

- Organic ghee (to be stored on a counter),
- Extra virgin olive oil (only to eat raw, not for cooking!! Look for PDO or something similar; most of the olive oil in the supermarket has been diluted with canola oil so read labels. You need to make sure it is real and that it really comes from the place it mentions, mainly Spain or Italy.),
- Raw cold pressed coconut oil,
- Red palm oil,
- Avocado oil,
- Flaxseed oil,
- Hemp seed oil.

BUYING DRINKS

Try not to drink store-bought juices or teas. Their ingredients lists are usually scary plus most of them are pasteurized (during pasteurization juices are brought to high temperatures where all nutrients from the fruits are killed, so you are basically drinking water full of bad ingredients and sugars. Definitely not worth it!!! Blend your own juice!!). But in case you want to buy some drinks go for the following:

- Veggie and fruit juices (organic, unpasteurized, cold pressed),
- Coconut water (unpasteurized, not from concentrate, raw),
- Nut milks (containing no sugar or carrageenan),
- Ice teas (look for unsweetened; no added sugars or sugar substitutes),
- Kombucha (no added sugars).

EATING OUT
– VS –
COOKING at HOME

As a total food enthusiast I love eating out! I love getting to know new places, having a chitchatting night with friends or family. But let's be honest, eating out can be really bad for your body nutrition-wise (and your budget!). It's not easy to find a restaurant where you are confident of the quality of the ingredients used. You don't know what oils they use, how clean their kitchen is, and what energy they put into your food!!! (Yes! There is a lot of energy transfer through cooking!)

Also remember that during your pregnancy you can easily get heartburn, acid reflux and feel extremely heavy after eating. In addition you need to be extra careful about the food you eat to avoid food poisoning and harmful bacteria reaching your baby. And let's not talk about what it costs to be eating out all the time! So it's better to eat more at home throughout the week and leave eating out for the weekends. Trust me it's only a matter of organizing yourself and cooking strategically in bulk things you could easily transform into different dishes; I will give you some tips to inspire your inner chef! Let's talk a little more about Eating out VS Cooking at home!

Eating out

For me eating out is "The Plan" so I love it! I go online and do research on new places offering real food. I love trying new healthy places where I can find juices, yummy bowls and farm-to-table options. Before being pregnant, in addition to the local farm-to-table options, I loved sushi or Peruvian food, where I had options such as sashimi, nigiri or makis (avoiding fried, asking for brown rice substitutes and dipping in tamari sauce instead of soy, which tends to be full of GMOs and MSG), and fresh ceviche! But also remember wherever you go to make smart choices from what is offered - that's the secret!

These are some cool tips to consider when eating out:

(It's incredible how much you can get from the chef and kitchen just by being friendly to the restaurant staff! You just have to ask nicely! And show your belly a little!)

If you don't have many options order any quality protein with vegetables. Almost everywhere you can substitute bad carbs in the dish for fresh salad or vegetables. Even with a burger you can go bunless and change it for lettuce.

Ask for sauces and dressings on the side and add ¼ of the portion. I usually dip the fork in the dressing and eat my salad.

Avoid eating the bread served as a starter (unless it's artisan, yumm!). If you are too tempted just order a side salad as a starter or a veggie appetizer!

Stop eating when you feel 80% full OR if you know portions are huge, tell your server you want ½ of your plate to go before it is served OR share as a couple! One main dish and one large salad for both!

Make sure your proteins are fully cooked to avoid food poisoning and bacteria.

Eat raw veggies only in places where you know fresh organic produce is served.

If you really want something get it and enjoy it! Don't feel guilty. Life is about balance and moderation. Also remember it's a matter of learning how to listen to your body and translating what it is asking for (think deconstructing the craving discussed in the "Quick & Dirty Lifesaving Tips" section). Also as I mentioned earlier, if you really want to go for that pain au chocolat you love, eat it! Have in mind industrialized foods are produced in masses, generally with poor quality ingredients, so just try to find an artisan bakery, where you know good ingredients are being used! Pair it with a cup of hot chocolate and enjoy!! (I know chocolate on top of chocolate, I'm mad about chocolate). Try to find better versions of the food you want, that's the trick.

Cooking at home

Ok for me there is nothing like home cooked meals! You know what exactly is in your food regarding ingredients, as well as the energetic component. You know the amount and quality of salt and oils used for cooking!! AND the mood swings and bad energy from a stressed and hectic restaurant kitchen won't go into your food!!! Yes I'm serious! This does happen! Just think why your mom's chicken soup always tastes so yummy and instantly cures your flu! It's because she cooks with love and with the intention of nurturing you; that's the type of energy you want in your food!!

I know that time is the main reason why people end up eating out or ordering food delivery. But I promise if you organize yourself you can make it!! Throughout my pregnancy I ate 95% of my meals at home and that was a crucial reason why I did sooo well (in addition to staying active and healthy in mind and body), my feet were never swollen and my heartburn only appeared when my belly was really, really huge!!

So give cooking a try! It's great to engage your partner in cooking too! Do it together as a plan, you can have a glass of wine, play some music, and dance a little too! You don't have to be the best cooks, but just because you're doing it together the outcome will be yummy! And full of love! That is always the best ingredient that makes food so fulfilling for your tummy and heart! (I will give you no sweat recipes for you to follow!!) In this way you won't only control the quality of foods making up your baby, as well as your weight gain, heartburn and acidity, but also your wallet! Plus that day on the weekend that you go and eat out will be really fun and special; it makes it more exciting!

These are some very useful tips for making home cooking easier and more enjoyable:

Make your trip to the grocery store a fun journey! Go prepared, take your lists (based on what you plan to cook during the week) and try always buying a new veggie or fruit and experiment with it!

When you go home with the groceries organize your fridge strategically (fruits here, veggies there, etc.). An organized fridge will motivate you!

Reserve some time during the week to do some prep like chopping some veggies to have them ready for some scrambled eggs, a stir fry, or to toss a quick salad.

Cook always a little more; remember your dinner could be your next day's lunch! Also this way you can have leftovers to be transformed into other meals (in the "Recipes" section I'll give you lots of options to cook and save!! And even freeze!). Buy some glass airtight containers! They work great for this purpose!

Some time-saving examples of batch cooking are:

- Quinoa, brown rice, other grains and pastas: cooked unseasoned can be used as a side dish, in a salad, in a soup or as a sweet porridge in the morning. With extra pasta you can drizzle a little oil on it and save in the fridge to toss a cold tuna salad the next day!

Example recipes: Brown Rice Porridge (pg. 128), Collard Green Salmon Wrap (pg. 159), Coconut Curried Lentils & Quinoa (pg. 181)

- Homemade dressings: can be stored for weeks in the fridge to use in a salad, as a spread, on toast, or as a marinade!

Example recipes: "To use as a Dressing, Spread or Dip!" (pg. 140)

- Homemade pancakes, waffles and other baked goods: can be stored in an airtight container and then frozen. When you are ready to consume them just use a bread toaster (works best for pancakes or waffles) or a small oven.

Example recipes: Green Waffles (pg. 126), Flourless Bagels (pg. 136), Flourless Hemp Brownies (pg. 210), Carrot-Banana Muffins (pg. 212)

- Baked veggies: whenever I'm using my oven I bake a batch of veggies; this saves me energy, mine and on the bills, and lots of time. I store those baked veggies in the fridge and then use them throughout the week as side dishes, tossed in salads or scrambled eggs or blended into soups with some stock or coconut milk!

Example recipes: Rustic Sweet Potato Frittata (pg. 133), Roasted Cauliflower & Tahini Soup (pg. 154), Mashed Sweet Potato (pg. 174)

I hope you feel motivated to get in the kitchen! Once you get on track it will go so smoothly you will feel like a pro!

Mommy to Be
PANTRY LISTS

VEGETABLES

- [ ] Kale
- [ ] Collard greens
- [ ] Spinach
- [ ] Asparagus
- [ ] Bell peppers
- [ ] Butter lettuce
- [ ] Romaine lettuce
- [ ] Watercress
- [ ] Arugula
- [ ] Broccoli
- [ ] Beets
- [ ] Butternut squash
- [ ] Onion
- [ ] Chives
- [ ] Scallions
- [ ] Cauliflower
- [ ] Radishes
- [ ] Brussels sprouts
- [ ] Beets
- [ ] Corn
- [ ] Celery
- [ ] Carrots
- [ ] Artichokes
- [ ] Mushrooms
- [ ] Eggplant
- [ ] Bok choy
- [ ] Garlic
- [ ] Shallots

GREAT HEALTHY OILS

- [ ] Extra virgin coconut oil
- [ ] Grass-fed butter
- [ ] Grass-fed ghee
- [ ] Cold-pressed olive oil
- [ ] Red palm oil
- [ ] Sesame oil
- [ ] Hemp oil
- [ ] Avocado oil
- [ ] Flaxseed oil
- [ ] Nut butters (no added sugars or oils)

COMPLEX CARBS

(Whole grains, Breads, Pasta +)

- [ ] Sweet potato
- [ ] Quinoa, amaranth and other ancient grains (spelt, millet, kamut, sorghum)
- [ ] Brown rice
- [ ] Sprouted grain breads, English muffins (frozen section or artisan)
- [ ] Sprouted grain tortilla (frozen section or artisan)
- [ ] Sprouted grain pastas
- [ ] Soba buckwheat noodles
- [ ] Bean and lentil pasta
- [ ] Almond flour or almond meal
- [ ] Flaxseed flour or flaxseed meal
- [ ] Old-fashioned oats or rolled oats
- [ ] Steel-cut oats
- [ ] Coconut flour

- [ ] Spelt flour
- [ ] Rice crackers
- [ ] Sushi nori wraps from the Pacific

LEGUMES

- [ ] Black beans
- [ ] Red kidney or cannellini beans
- [ ] Chickpeas or garbanzo beans
- [ ] Peas
- [ ] Lentils
- [ ] BPA-free canned versions of the above

NUTS & SEEDS

- [ ] Cashews
- [ ] Peanuts
- [ ] Walnuts
- [ ] Almonds
- [ ] Pistachios
- [ ] Macadamia nuts
- [ ] Pecans
- [ ] Flax seeds
- [ ] Pumpkin seeds
- [ ] Sunflower seeds
- [ ] Sesame seeds
- [ ] Chia seeds
- [ ] Hemp seeds
- [ ] Almond butter
- [ ] Peanut butter

FRUITS

- [ ] Papaya
- [ ] Oranges
- [ ] Strawberry
- [ ] Grapefruit
- [ ] Raspberries
- [ ] Blueberries
- [ ] Pineapple
- [ ] Avocado
- [ ] Figs
- [ ] Kiwi
- [ ] Bananas
- [ ] Limes
- [ ] Apples
- [ ] Pears
- [ ] Watermelon
- [ ] Pomegranate
- [ ] Dragon fruit
- [ ] Ginger root
- [ ] Turmeric root

DRIED FRUIT

- [ ] Dates
- [ ] Figs
- [ ] Goji berries
- [ ] Golden berries
- [ ] Mulberries
- [ ] Currants

FROZEN FRUIT

- [ ] Strawberries
- [ ] Mixed berries
- [ ] Blueberries

- [ ] Mango
- [ ] Pineapple
- [ ] Acai

ANIMAL PROTEIN

- [ ] Pastured, organic eggs
- [ ] Wild salmon
- [ ] Wild corvina/halibut
- [ ] Grass-fed beef
- [ ] Organic free-range chicken
- [ ] Wild-caught shrimp
- [ ] Lamb
- [ ] Organic turkey
- [ ] Nitrate-free organic turkey bacon
- [ ] Canned sardines
- [ ] Canned wild tuna

DAIRY

- [ ] Organic kefir (no added sugar)
- [ ] Organic plain Greek yogurt (no added sugar)
- [ ] Pasteurized sheep feta cheese
- [ ] Organic grass-fed hard cheeses (cow's, sheep's, goat's)
- [ ] Pasteurized cottage cheese
- [ ] Pasteurized mozzarella and bocconcini
- [ ] Whole organic grass-fed milk

NATURAL FLAVORINGS

- [ ] Himalayan pink salt / kosher salt / sea salt
- [ ] Turmeric
- [ ] Curry
- [ ] Paprika
- [ ] Cayenne pepper

- [ ] Ginger powder
- [ ] Cinnamon powdered & sticks
- [ ] Cloves
- [ ] Coriander
- [ ] Garlic and onion powder
- [ ] Cumin
- [ ] Crushed red pepper
- [ ] Nutmeg
- [ ] Pepper
- [ ] Miso paste (I like white miso)
- [ ] Tahini or sesame seed paste
- [ ] Whole grain mustard
- [ ] Yellow mustard
- [ ] Dijon mustard
- [ ] Balsamic vinegar
- [ ] Raw apple cider vinegar
- [ ] Rice wine vinegar
- [ ] Tamari sauce
- [ ] Ponzu sauce
- [ ] Hot sauce (unsweetened)
- [ ] Basil (fresh)
- [ ] Rosemary (fresh)
- [ ] Thyme (fresh)
- [ ] Parsley (fresh)
- [ ] Cilantro (fresh)
- [ ] Dill (fresh)
- [ ] Oregano (dried)
- [ ] Unsweetened whole coconut milk
- [ ] Pickles (no food dyes)
- [ ] Olives
- [ ] Sesame seeds
- [ ] Madagascar bourbon vanilla beans
- [ ] Sauerkraut

SWEETENERS

- [ ] Maple syrup
- [ ] Raw unfiltered honey
- [ ] Coconut palm sugar

- [ ] Unsweetened chocolate / stevia-sweetened
- [ ] Agave nectar
- [ ] Stevia leaf (whole leaf stevia, not extract)

EXTRA SUPERFOODS

- [ ] Raw cacao nibs
- [ ] Raw cacao powder
- [ ] Powdered spirulina
- [ ] Powdered maca
- [ ] Powdered moringa leaf

DRINKS

- [ ] Raw coconut water
- [ ] Kombucha
- [ ] Organic cold-pressed veggie juice

FOR BAKING

- [ ] Baking soda
- [ ] Aluminium-free baking powder

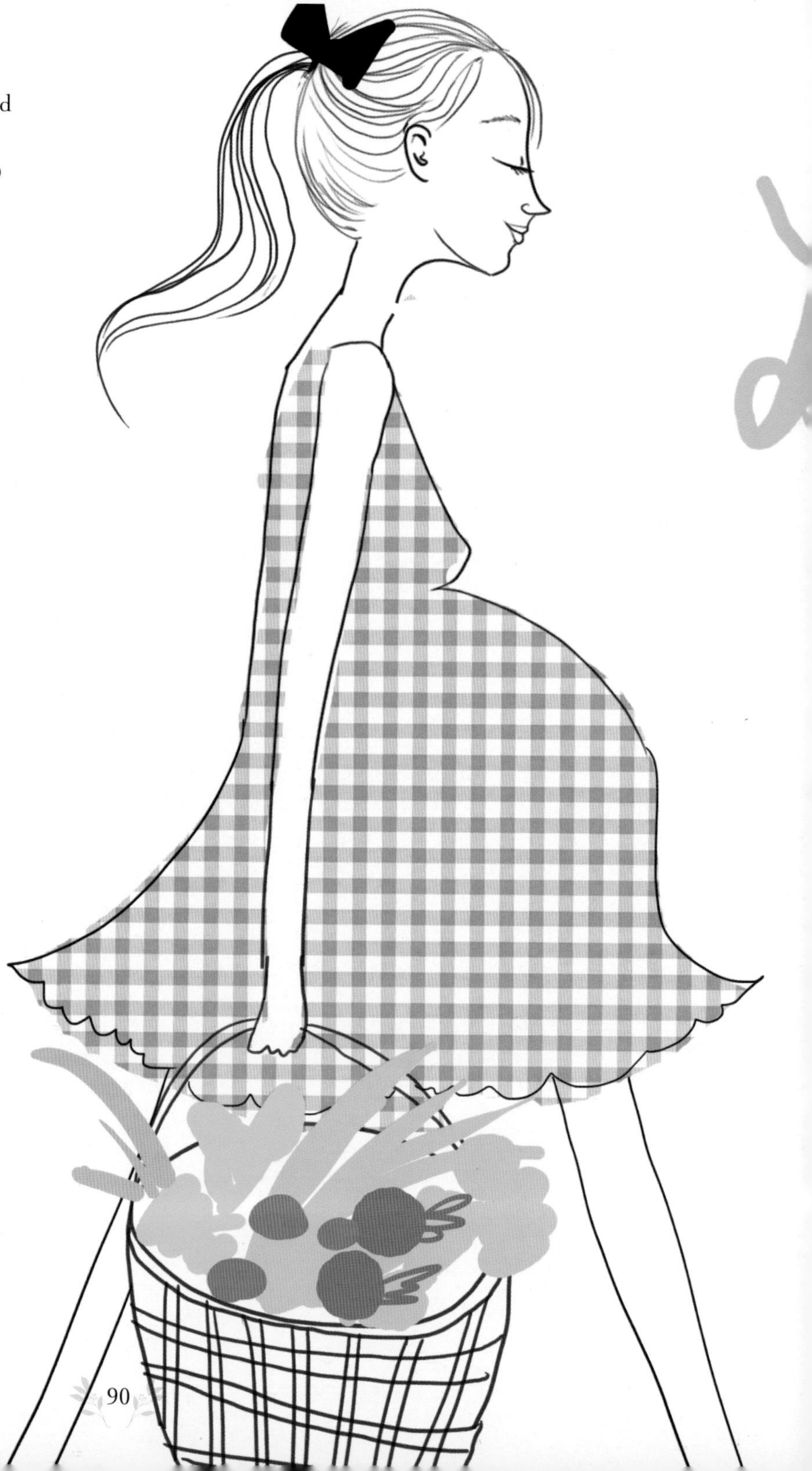

Let's eat more REAL food

Follow our
EXTRA
GOODIES
link to
download!
WWW.FFTHMIAMI.COM/
EXTRA-GOODIES

III. Recipes:

Let's get hands to work!

RECIPES

Yaay!!! We finally get to this part!! My favorite!!! I'm sharing with you some recipes that don't require extra expertise to be made! I focus on ingredients that are great for us mommies-to-be! Rich in those vitamins and minerals we especially need during the most blessed months in our lives, but could also be enjoyed by all the family!!! They are easy, versatile, yummy and healthy!! I included some of my all-time favorites too, of course!!!

Please, please DO read all the intros for each recipe!

All my tips and secrets!! Because my goal here is not only to give you one recipe and stop there, but to teach you the main technique and idea and leave room for you to experiment, to let your imagination fly! Try with other ingredients, transform dishes, and really engage in your cooking by making it 100% enjoyable and part of your everyday routine. So you'll find tips such as cooking in bulk, using leftovers from one recipe to make the next or how to transform that dinner to breakfast... lots of cool things!! I want you to fall madly in love with cooking like me!!! And easy, breezy, enjoyable and healthy cooking done completely From the Heart!

Please have the following things in mind when following my recipes:

All ingredients used are the best quality possible. Please refer to "Mommy-To-Be Pantry Lists" section for specifics on ingredients to buy.

 Specifics on organics and required labels on foods are not included in the ingredient list of the recipe because it will make it sooooo wordy!!! So have in mind I use The Dirty Dozen™ and The Clean Fifteen™ lists in the "Organics: To Buy or Not to Buy?" section. Plus if you need more specifics for other products such as animal proteins, dairy and oils, they are in the section "Reading Food Labels & Shopping Tips." So for example, if in a recipe I mention celery, I refer to "organic celery." If I say eggs, I refer to pastured organic eggs, if I say butter or milk I refer to organic grass-fed milk and butter, etc.

 The oils used for cooking are coconut oil, ghee, butter, red palm oil and avocado oil (love for grilling!). So you can use them interchangeably!

 The oils used for dressings (to use cold) are extra virgin olive oil, hemp seed oil and flaxseed oil.

 The salt used is UNREFINED. I always use Himalayan pink salt, but you can also go for kosher salt or sea salt.

 When I call for stock you can make your own (in the recipe "My Mommy's Soup," pg. 152) or use a "clean" store-bought version! Remember all the tips about reading labels! It must look like a recipe; no weird, unpronounceable names. The one I buy goes like this: water, organic chicken, organic onion, organic apple cider vinegar, organic rosemary extract. So as long as the ingredients are good you can save some time when you don't have that much! The same goes with BPA-free canned beans, like chickpeas and black beans.

 All beans must be soaked overnight. To improve digestibility and gases add a bay leaf or garlic clove when cooking, or cumin or vinegar in the last minutes of cooking.

 All pans and pots used are Teflon-free. Teflon contains the chemicals PFC and PFOA which can be transferred to our food and air (when the heat gets over 450 °F or 230 °C and the coating gets deteriorated with scratches then toxic particles and gases are emitted). So choose PFC- and PFOA-free nonstick pans (they are referred to as greener nonstick. Avoid the word Teflon); stainless steel and cast iron are safer options. But, if you have to stick with your Teflon pans just keep in mind to control the temperature and to replace them when you see signs of deterioration!

Essential & Basic utensils we are using

Mandoline Slicer

Donut Pan

Veggie Spiralizer

Measuring spoons

Muffin Pan

Mixing Bowl

Food processor

Whisk

Measuring Cup

Waffle maker

High speed blender

Nut Bag

Strainer

♥ Love!

Please have lots of fun and remember to always add the best
secret ingredient to all my recipes: LOVE!

First some juicing 101 (or I must say "Smoothing" 101). I know there are a lot of unanswered questions regarding juices. With all the juicing hysteria, you hear things like cold-pressed, centrifugal juicer, slow juicer or blended juices. I will break it down easily for you to choose the road you want to take! Personally after being a juicer fan for years, I gave blending a chance and now I just loveee my high-performance blender to death and I use it every day!!! Remember you always want to have lots of greens in those smoothies and juices! Fruits are yummy but only adding fruit will be lots of sugar! (Yes, sugar in its natural source but too much of it still increases your blood sugar levels! Remember portion size is key!) So try to shoot for a ratio of something like 3:1 veggies to fruits!

If you are using a juicer the juice will be thinner as the pulp of the fruits is being discarded by the machine. Centrifugal juicers are usually cheaper but they destroy almost all the enzymes and nutrients in veggies and fruits. An optimal option then is to spend a little more money (or spend a little less on shoes!!!) and invest in a good slow juicer. These slowly extract the juice from fruits and vegetables without losing any nutritional value.

A general formula for juices using a juicer is:

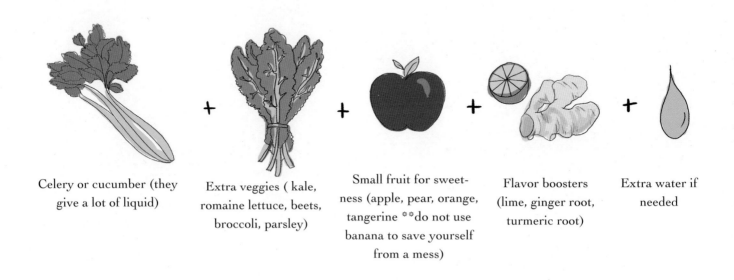

Celery or cucumber (they give a lot of liquid)

Extra veggies (kale, romaine lettuce, beets, broccoli, parsley)

Small fruit for sweetness (apple, pear, orange, tangerine **do not use banana to save yourself from a mess)

Flavor boosters (lime, ginger root, turmeric root)

Extra water if needed

If you go for store-bought juices look for organic, unpasteurized, and cold-pressed juices. They should have a short shelf life so anything in tetra paks or cans.

Last but not least, using my beloved blender!!!!! In this option, it is not only easier to clean, but you also get the whole fiber from veggies and fruits so the outcome is a more fulfilling juice or smoothie with the nutrient quota intact!! Yayyy, two things we love! To feel satisfied and nourished! Sooo the following recipes will all be done using a high performance blender!

The procedure for all of the recipes below is the same: blend all ingredients until smooth and garnish with your favorite toppings! I alwaysss go crazy with toppings from bee pollen to goji berries, chia seeds, hemp seeds, cacao nibs, dried coconut, and nuts! You name it!!! You can have these smoothies in the morning, for snacks or when you feel like having something sweet!!

Hint Hint: Smoothies are a great opportunity to sneak in some superfoods and extra boosters like spirulina, turmeric, moringa leaf, maca, etc.! Let your imagination fly!

LIQUID VEGGIES

SERVES 1

This is my base power smoothie! I try having it every morning around 10 minutes after my tall glass of room temperature water. I love starting my day with lots of greens! I feel every cell in my body being nourished from this healthy start! I do a lot of variations of this smoothie (depending on what I have in my fridge!!! I sometimes add broccoli, romaine lettuce….). You can add some liquid if it's too dense for you and an extra ½ banana or ¼ cup pineapple if you want an easier introduction into veggie smoothies.

1 medium cucumber

2 stalks celery

2 lemons (juice)

1 green apple

1 t fresh ginger root

1 cup kale

1 cup spinach

2 stalks parsley

4 asparagus

Greenie Love ♥

HUBBY'S FAVE

REFRESH YOU

VERY BERRY

FLESH

in Paradise

VERY BERRY

SERVES 1

½ cup frozen strawberries

½ cup frozen blueberries

½ cup frozen raspberries

2 cups spinach

1 cup liquid nut milk/yogurt

2 T goji berries + some to garnish

IN PARADISE

SERVES 1

½ cup frozen pineapple

½ cup frozen mango

1 kiwi

2 cups kale

1 t turmeric powder/1 inch root turmeric

1 cup coconut water

Coconut flakes and fresh kiwi to garnish

HUBBY'S FAVE

SERVES 1

3 T cacao powder

1 T cinnamon

½ frozen banana

1 T peanut butter

2 T hemp seeds

1 cup almond milk

2 t powdered maca

1 cup ice

Cocoa nibs to garnish

REFRESH YOUR FLESH

SERVES 1

½ cup frozen pineapple

2 cups spinach

1 t fresh ginger root

1 T mint/1 stalk + some to garnish

1 medium cucumber

1 t raw unfiltered honey

1 t powdered moringa leaf

½ cup coconut water

Drink up!

GREENIE LOVE

SERVES 1

1 cup kale

1 cup spinach

1 t powdered spirulina

2 dates

½ frozen banana

½ cup coconut water

1 t chia seeds to garnish

These two dairy-free milk alternatives are great for those who don't tolerate milk very well, and for those who do too!!! With these recipes I made my husband actually like almond milk!! It was the only healthy food he preferred not to have, before this yummy version of course. The taste of homemade almond and hemp milk is so yummy, creamy and delicate compared to store-bought, plus you don't have the nasty added ingredients for shelf life. Remember, if you go for store-bought versions, check ingredient lists (no added sugars or carrageenan).

You can make this every week and keep in the fridge to eat with cereal, add to smoothies or sipped chilled with your favorite straw!

Drink up!

HEMP MILK

SERVES 7

1 cup hemp milk
5 cups filtered water
4 pitted dates/maple syrup or honey to taste
½ t Himalayan pink salt
½ Madagascar bourbon vanilla bean

1. Add hemp seeds and water to a blender at high speed for approximately 40-60 seconds, until the seeds are completely pulverized.

2. If you want to strain it use a nut bag or cheese strainer. (I love mine unstrained to feel the fiber from the seeds a little!) Discard the pulp or add it to your oatmeal or cereal bowl.

3. With a knife open the vanilla bean and scrape off the seeds (enjoy the yummy aroma from real vanilla!!).

4. Rinse the blender and add the milk; blend in the salt, dates/maple syrup and vanilla seeds.

5. Store in a glass airtight container (stick in the used vanilla bean for extra flavor!) in the fridge for up to a week!! For chocolate version add 1T of raw cacao powder!!

Drink up!

ALMOND MILK

SERVES 7

2 cups almonds

5 cups filtered water

4 pitted dates/maple syrup or honey to taste

½ t Himalayan pink salt

½ Madagascar bourbon vanilla bean

1. Soak almonds in filtered water overnight or a little more for a creamier texture!

2. Drain water, rinse almonds and add them to a blender with 4 cups of water at high speed for one minute.

3. This one you do need to always strain using a cheese strainer or nut bag. Use your strong arms to squeeze all the milk out (this is a workout too!!). Remove the almond pulp from the bag and save it! You can add it to your oatmeal, baked goods or ground meat (as a bonding agent) when cooking patties or meatballs!!

4. Rinse blender and add back the milk, the extra cup of filtered water, salt, dates/maple syrup and vanilla seeds (for vanilla use step 3 from Hemp Milk recipe!!). Blend until smooth.

5. Store in a glass airtight container (stick in the used vanilla bean for extra flavor!) in the fridge for up to a week!! For chocolate version add 1T of raw cacao powder!!

The miracles of the ultra-cool ginger root....

Ginger is not only great to control your nausea, morning sickness and motion sickness, but is also the star ingredient in our natural immunity shot!! Thanks to its anti-inflammatory and antioxidant properties, it smoothes the throat and eases aches and pain! Also in our natural remedy against the flu we add some other powerful ingredients that fight bacteria and infection and give your immune system a boost:

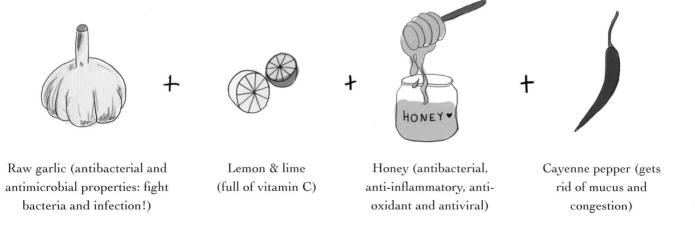

Raw garlic (antibacterial and antimicrobial properties: fight bacteria and infection!)

Lemon & lime (full of vitamin C)

Honey (antibacterial, anti-inflammatory, anti-oxidant and antiviral)

Cayenne pepper (gets rid of mucus and congestion)

BYE BYE
NAUSEA &
FLU KICK ASS

Drink up!

BYE-BYE NAUSEA

SERVES 1

2 T ginger, minced

1 T raw unfiltered honey

2 cups cold filtered water

1. Mince ginger very finely with a knife or using a food processor.

2. To an airtight container like a jar, add the ginger, water and honey. Close the jar and shake it, shake it, shake it, like a professional bartender.

3. Add some ice and enjoy cold! You can actually triple portions and store in the fridge for a week! So you can have a glass every day you feel your nausea coming!

Drink up!

FLU KICK-ASS

SERVES 1 SHOT

1 t ginger, minced

1 small clove garlic or ½ regular size, minced

1 t raw unfiltered honey

2 lime juice

¼ t cayenne pepper

1. Mince garlic and ginger root very finely with a knife or using a food processor.

2. In a shot glass combine the lime juice, minced ginger, garlic, honey and cayenne pepper.

3. Bottoms up! If you feel a cold is coming or you are just in need of an immunity boost, feel free to take one shot in the morning and one shot in the afternoon every day as needed; it works wonderfully! As with the nausea drink, you can pre-batch and store it in the fridge!

I grew up drinking huge cups of hot chocolate in my grandma's house. It was my favorite part of breakfast! We did what is called in that region of Colombia "migote," meaning we could throw in cheese, crackers, bread and even arepa in pieces and then eat everything with a spoon!! So I came up with this version to drink whenever I feel I need a little bit of home, plus I just love how maca goes with chocolate! Soooo delicious. This is perfect for a cold morning when you want something creamy and rich!

Drink up!

MACA HOT CACAO

SERVES 1

1 cup homemade almond milk or regular milk

1 T raw powdered cacao

1 t cloves

1 stick cinnamon

1 t maca

1. In a small sauce pan add almond milk or your favorite milk, cloves and cinnamon stick and heat on medium heat until just before it boils.

2. Remove pan from heat and add the powdered cacao and maca; whisk vigorously (using your hand whisk! Yes more arm work!) until completely dissolved and some foam forms on the top.

3. I love the strong taste from the raw cacao but if you prefer you can sweeten a little with coconut palm sugar. Serve in your lucky mug and enjoy!!

4. Add some organic cheese if you want to give "migote" a try! We use one similar to queso fresco (called "cuajada") but during pregnancy it is better to avoid those types of cheese so try with mozzarella!! Still yummy!

Maca Hot Cacao

Although I didn't include acai berries in my "Superfoods for Supermommas" section, their beauty and libido superpowers are well known thanks to their high content of antioxidants. My first real "encounter" with this yumminess was in Brazil, when I went for two months all over the country following the World Cup. OMG I became obsessed with acai bowls and ate a minimum of one every day! They sold them everywhere, and just walking along the beach, you could see the beautiful palms with their acai berries hanging like waterfalls.

Luckily for me acai had just recently reached the US markets, sold in frozen packages to be blended at home!! You can buy these at your health store or even online! Just make sure there are no added sugars. Acai can also be added to smoothies and juices!

If you don't have access to frozen acai, just use frozen blueberries (1 cup to replace one package of acai); they are yummy and high in antioxidants too.

AND off course, this acai bowl wouldn't be nearly as bowl-licking good if it weren't for my Superfoods Granola!! The secret of this granola is the quinoa and amaranth base. In addition to its protein content (and awesome nutritional value), it gives a unique crunchiness and nutty flavor. I hate buying store-bought granola; they always trick you with ads like "100% Natural" or "50 calories per serving," and when you go and look at the ingredient lists, they are full of S** nasty oils and all types of added sugars. So the solution is very easy, bake your own!! With real, simple ingredients!!

For the following granola recipe you can use the base (quinoa, amaranth, rolled oats baked with maple syrup and coconut oil), and get creative by adding your favorite nuts, dried fruits and seeds!!

erfoods Granola

ACAI BOWL WITH SUPERFOODS GRANOLA

SERVES 1

2 cups old fashioned rolled oats

1 cup dry quinoa

1 cup dry amaranth

½ cup coconut oil

¼ cup maple syrup

1 T cinnamon

⅓ cup whole almonds

⅓ cup chopped walnuts

⅓ cup pumpkin seeds

⅓ unsweetened dried coconut

2 T hemp seeds

2 T chia seeds

2 T flax seeds

⅓ cup dried golden berries

⅓ cup dried goji berries

⅓ cup dried mulberries

2 t spirulina powder

Granola

1. Preheat oven to 325°F or 163°C.

2. In a deep bowl mix oats, quinoa, coconut oil, maple syrup, cinnamon, hemp seeds, chia seeds, flax seeds, almonds, walnuts, pumpkin seeds and coconut. Massage with your hands making sure all ingredients are well-mixed.

3. Spread the mixture evenly on a baking sheet. Use a silicon mat or baking paper underneath for better results.

4. Place in the oven and using a wooden spoon move the mixture around every 15 minutes for 35-40 minutes (we don't want it to burn!! So be careful because it can happen in the blink of an eye!!).

5. If it looks toasted and tanned it's ready to be taken out of the oven!

6. Wait a little for it to cool down. Then add the spirulina (we want it raw, that's why we add it at the end), golden berries, goji berries and mulberries; mix well.

7. Store in an airtight container and keep fresh on countertop for months!! There you have a plan for a lazy Sunday; bake granola for your whole semester!

120

1 frozen package of acai no sugar added (if you can't find replace with 1 cup frozen blueberries)
½ banana
½ cup pineapple
4 cups kale

Acai

1. Add everything to the blender and blend until smooth (you'll have to stop the blender and scrape everything down with a spatula and blend again, until completely smooth).

2. Pour in a bowl and sprinkle your yummy Superfoods Granola on top.

3. Usually I add 1 T of peanut butter or almond butter if I want an extra protein boost! (Plus healthy fats control blood sugar levels when eating fruit!! So always eat fruit with a healthy fat!)

DIY CEREAL

Just as with granola, store-bought cereal tends to be very sneaky with hidden, nasty ingredients. I'll give you this cool option to which you can easily add your personal touch. Just keep the crunchy base with your popped grains and personalize it with your favorite nuts, sliced apricots or dates, some cinnamon...options are infinite! Mix everything and save in an airtight container to leave on the counter!

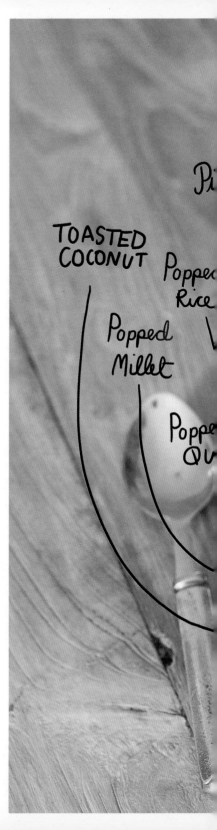

:TIP!:
You can add some
GRANOLA to
make it more
CRUNCHY

hios

Popped
Kamut

ALMONDS

Mulberries

CHIA
FLAX
& HEMP
SEEDS

ALMOND
MILK!

Popped
Amaranth

GOJI
BERRIES

Golden
Berries

CHOCO-CASHEW
cream
GREEN
WAFFLE SANDWICH

CHOCO-CASHEW-CREAM GREEN WAFFLE SANDWICH

As a declared sweet-tooth, there were mornings during my pregnancy when I only wanted something sweet!! Obviously something nutritiously sweet; sooo I came up with these green waffles and the most amazing Nutella-beating chocolate cashew cream!!!! You can premake these waffles and take them on the go as a snack. The coolest thing is that you can freeze them for up to a month and throw them in the toaster for a quick breakfast fix!

Choco-Cashew Cream

serves 8

2 cups raw unsalted cashews

6 T cacao powder

6 T coconut oil

2 T raw unfiltered honey

1. Blend cashews in a food processor or blender for around 5 minutes until smooth (you'll have to stop the blender and scrape everything down with a spatula and blend again, until completely smooth; you will see that it turns from ground nuts to a cream!).

2. Add the cacao powder, melted coconut oil and honey. Blend for another minute and ta-da! Save in an airtight container or jar!

Green Waffles makes

3 whole waffles

1 egg

1 ripe banana

1 cup old fashioned oats

2 cups spinach

2 prunes or pitted dates

2 T apple cider vinegar

½ cup nut milk

1 T cinnamon

2 T spirulina powder

1 t baking soda

1. Add all ingredients to a blender and blend until smooth.

2. Preheat waffle maker and with a brush grease both sides of the iron with some coconut oil (you can use a paper towel if you don't have a brush!).

3. Start pouring the mixture slowly in the center; let the mixture extend until just before it reaches the edge of the iron (so it doesn't overflow when you close it, and you don't have to clean a mess!).

4. Wait until the waffle maker tells you it's ready. Do not open before or your waffle will be ruined. A sign that they are done is that the steam produced stops!

5. I love my waffles toasty brown, but if you are freezing them try to cook them just a little less.

6. Note in the picture that my waffle iron makes rounded waffles. From one waffle I make 2 mini sandwiches.

7. Spread the choco-cashew cream all the way to the edges, add some walnuts, sliced banana and seeds (plus whatever extra fillings you want!). Close the sandwich with another waffle, add some maple syrup if you want and it's ready to be devoured!

BROWN RICE PORRIDGE

SERVES 4

From a lullaby during childhood to every Christmas mingle, rice porridge (fancy name for our Colombian "Arroz con Leche") was everywhere. So it was natural for me to come up with a healthy version of this, for those mornings during pregnancy when I wanted something warm and heartful. (It almost warms up my soul! Making me feel at home!) You can also follow the same recipe using quinoa! Or go for a savory porridge adding some stock, turkey bacon, some al dente asparagus heads, and some real parmesan cheese, yummmm!! This is a great way to use brown rice leftovers (just remember to cook the brown rice unseasoned (no salt, cooked in water), so you can easily transform it into sweet and savory dishes!!).

1 cup brown rice

1 cup water

2 cups milk / nut milk

1 cinnamon stick

6 T hemp seeds

1 T maple syrup

⅓ cup walnuts, chopped

½ cup fresh berries (strawberries, blackberries, blueberries)

½ t spirulina powder (optional)

Procedure if cooking brown rice from scratch:

1. Rinse brown rice under running water until the water is clear.

2. In a pot bring rice, cinnamon stick, water and milk to a boil and reduce heat; cover and let it simmer for approximately 30 minutes (try one grain to know it's ready!).

3. Add hemp seeds, maple syrup and walnuts (and spirulina if you are using it).

4. Serve into bowl, add fresh berries and mint. Drizzle some extra maple syrup on top and eat right away!!

5. If you want it creamier you can add more milk or high quality cream. (If you are eating porridge leftovers from the fridge, warm them up in a small pot adding a little bit of milk to give it texture!)

Procedure if using brown rice leftovers:

1. For 1 cup of leftover rice add 1 cup of milk, the same amounts of cinnamon, hemp seeds, and maple syrup from the recipe. Combine everything and heat on the stove for 8 minutes.

2. Add spirulina if using, fresh berries, and drizzle more maple syrup on top!

Brown Rice Poridge

BANANA & PEANUT BUTTER BAKED OATMEAL

SERVES 4

When I wake up feeling I could eat my whole fridge (almost every morning when pregnant), or when I know I'm having a busy morning running errands, I go for something fulfilling like oatmeal! I enjoy eating oatmeal so much! My two favorite ways of eating it are baked or raw! (Two ways in which starches are broken down better so it's easier to digest!) Both are extremely easy. **Raw Oatmeal** is simply old-fashioned oats or steel-cut (the difference is that steel-cut oats are less processed so have a more fibrous texture) soaked in your favorite milk (or even yogurt!!) overnight in the fridge (I usually add some chia seeds and a powdered superfood); then the next day I add some fresh fruit and nuts and that's it! It is a quick breakfast fix when you are in a hurry! ... And the following is my yummy Baked Oatmeal recipe, which I love because I feel I'm eating dessert for breakfast! You can bake a whole dish and eat it throughout the week! (Add a scoop of real ice cream, a drizzle of maple syrup and there you have a dessert!)

Banana & Peanut Butter
BAKED
oatmeal

2 cups old-fashioned oats or steel-cut oats

2 eggs

2 ½ cups milk/nut milk

4 bananas

4 T peanut butter

2 T maple syrup

1 t cinnamon

1 t aluminum-free baking powder

½ t Himalayan pink salt

1. Preheat oven to 375°F or 190°C.

2. Coat baking dishes with some butter or coconut oil. (You can use individual size dishes like I did or a large rectangular dish, either would work!)

3. Cut 2 bananas into small slices and arrange them on the bottom of the dishes. Drizzle some peanut butter on top.

4. Whisk eggs, milk, maple syrup and cinnamon in a bowl. Then add the oats, baking powder and salt.

5. Pour the oat mixture into the baking dish or small dishes. Decorate by thinly cutting the other bananas long ways and drizzling a little more peanut butter on top!

6. Bake for 30 minutes or until you see the oatmeal nice and gold! Then add some maple syrup before serving!! (I know 30 minutes seems like forever but it is really worth it.)

7. You can let your imagination fly and add berries in addition to the banana on the bottom, then a little more on the top with some nuts and ta-da!! Another yummy recipe. Have in mind that if you have the base recipe (oat mixture), you can go crazy with fruits, nuts and toppings!

RUSTIC SWEET POTATO TORTILLA

SERVES 4

As cliché as it may sound my absolutely favorite Spanish tapa is a beautifully and freshly cooked "tortilla." The way they perfectly season the eggs with simple ingredients and cook it to a moisture perfection is what kills me (in my opinion if one can cook yummy eggs, one is a chef! Eggs are so simple yet with so many flavor levels!). Of course, during my pregnancy when I thought about eating eggs, the first thing that came into my mind was to have them as a Spanish tortilla. One morning I experimented with this one, using sweet potato instead of white potato (it has a little more fiber) and adding handfuls of spinach (to sneak in some greens for my veggie daily quota during those days of nausea).

8 eggs

1 medium sweet potato

1 medium onion, chopped

1 medium bell pepper, sliced

4 cups fresh spinach

1 clove garlic, minced

3 stalks fresh parsley

1 t paprika

1 t turmeric

½ t black pepper

2 T ghee

1 t Himalayan pink salt

1. Thinly slice the pepper, removing the ribs and seeds; chop onion and garlic.

2. Peel and dice the sweet potato. (I love the rustic texture of diced potato, but you can slice them approximately an inch thick, like potatoes in a classic Spanish tortilla!)

3. In a natural non-stick pan heat 1 T ghee (I use ghee for sautéing a lot! Plus it gives potatoes a yummy flavor). Add onion, garlic, peppers and potato. Cook for about 10 minutes, and then add the spinach and cook for another 5 minutes or until you feel the potatoes are crisp and tender!

4. In a bowl whisk eggs, paprika, turmeric, pepper, salt, and some of the fresh parsley (really whisk using your strong arm that will be carrying that baby around soon!). Add the other T of ghee to the pan and, making sure the pan is hot, pour the whisked eggs on top of the veggies.

5. There are two options: you can either finish the tortilla in the oven, or if you feel encouraged to invert the tortilla, go for it!

6. If you go for the oven, bake the tortilla for 12-15 minutes at 375°F or 190°C until the tortilla is set (make sure your pan is like a skillet! All material ovenproof!).

7. If you want to invert the tortilla, lower heat to medium low heat and cook for about 8-10 minutes, until the bottom of the tortilla is set (you will see that the center will still be wet but the edges are beginning to set!). With a spatula let go of the edges if they are sticking to the pan.

8. The next move is somewhat difficult but so fun!! So be careful! Invert the tortilla onto a plate (at least as wide as your pan) and immediately slide the tortilla back onto the pan and cook for another 5-8 minutes more or until it is completely set!

9. Invert the cooked tortilla onto a plate, cut into four and garnish with more fresh parsley and some arugula!

STic *Sweet* POTATO & TORTiLLA

FLOURLESS BAGEL EGG SANDWICH

Is there something yummier than having an egg sandwich for breakfast? Yes! Baking your own flourless bagels! Let me tell you that I'm a fan of these bagels because they are so versatile! You can bake a batch and save in an airtight container, or even freeze for a month! If you want to go the sweet route you can change the condiments (paprika, garlic powder and onion powder) for cinnamon and cardamom! In this case I use them for a breakfast sandwich (with a yummy pastured egg and sautéed collard greens in the middle!!) Remember to sneak in greens everywhere!! This case is not an exception.

Bagels

Makes 12 Bagels

in a donut baking pan

4 eggs

¼ cup apple cider vinegar

1 cup milk/nut milk

1 cup almond meal/almond flour

2 t baking powder

1 t paprika

½ t garlic powder

½ t onion powder

1 t Himalayan pink salt

1. Preheat oven to 375°F or 190°C.

2. In a bowl whisk eggs, milk, apple cider vinegar, salt, paprika, garlic and onion powder (really whisk here so you can add some air into those eggs!). Then add almond meal and baking powder.

3. Pour the mixture into the donut baking pan and bake for 15 minutes.

Meanwhile…

Sandwich filling

Makes 2 sandwiches

4 pastured eggs

1 cup collard greens or your favorite leafy green, chopped

½ onion, chopped

½ garlic clove, minced

1 T ghee or butter

1 T sheep's feta cheese

1. In a pan add butter, ghee or red palm oil, and sauté onion, garlic and collard greens (you can use any leafy green you have at hand! Kale, spinach, mustard greens…) for around 5 minutes.

2. Cook your eggs in your favorite style! I poached mine. (Shhh! Don't tell anyone I left the inside runny!! You are not supposed to have undercooked eggs while pregnant for the risk of carrying salmonella bacteria. I use good quality eggs and pay a lot of attention to the handling. It is not supposed to be such a big deal, but if very very unlucky; salmonella will only make you sick, it won't reach your baby.) BUT, I guess the most convenient thing to do is to poach your eggs until the yolks are completely set!! Just in case!

3. To poach your egg (I do one at a time), take a pan and heat water with 1 t of salt and 2 t of white vinegar. When the water is simmering, stir water in one direction with a spatula, creating a whirlpool movement.

4. Immediately, carefully and slowly drop the egg in the middle of that whirlpool (make sure egg is fridge cold. It works better!!). Let the egg cook for 5 minutes and take it out of the water with a slotted spoon!

5. Make your bagel sandwich by adding the sautéed collard greens, your eggs (sprinkle some Himalayan pink salt!), some crumbled real cheese if you want, and ta-da!!

Sandwich ♥

& supper

SALAD

To use as a Dressing, Spread or Dip!

The following recipes can be used as marinades for your fish or veggies, as spreads for your sandwich or wrap, or as dips for those homemade chicken fingers or raw veggie sticks! They are soooo easy to make that there is literally no reason why one should continue buying store-bought sauces and vinaigrettes. Honestly, most of those are full of ingredients you don't want in your system and those healthy ones out there made with real ingredients can cost an arm and a leg!! Give the following a try! Plus you can prepare a little more and save for a week or two!

140

Dill & Yogurt sauce

KALE pesto

Balsamic
Vinaigrette

White
Truffle
Marinade

Spirulina
Dressing

Peanut-
Miso
sauce

Asiatic
Dressing

Honey
Mustard

MISO & PEANUT DIPPING SAUCE

(Collard Green Salmon Wrap pg. 159)

2 T white miso paste

2 T peanut butter

1 clove of garlic

½ t fresh ginger root

1 t rice vinegar

2 T agave nectar

¼ cup filtered water

1 t black sesame seeds

Process all ingredients using a food processor or blender. Store in an airtight container in the fridge for up to 3 weeks.

BALSAMIC VINAIGRETTE

¼ cup balsamic vinegar

¼ cup extra virgin olive oil

1 stalk fresh rosemary

½ t chili flakes

1 t paprika

1 clove of garlic

½ t Himalayan pink salt

In a bowl whisk all ingredients. Store in an airtight container and keep in a fresh cabinet or on a counter for several months.

HONEY MUSTARD

(Almond & Amaranth Crusted Fish Sandwich pg. 162)

1 T Dijon mustard

2 T whole grain mustard

1 T yellow mustard

1 T raw unfiltered honey

1 t apple cider vinegar

¼ cup plain Greek yogurt

¼ t Himalayan pink salt

In a bowl combine all ingredients. Store in an airtight container in the fridge for up to 3 weeks.

SPIRULINA DRESSING

¼ cup extra virgin olive oil

1 ½ t yellow mustard

1 lime (juice)

1 t powdered spirulina

¼ t Himalayan pink salt

1 t fresh cilantro

In a bowl combine all ingredients. Store in an airtight container in the fridge for up to a week.

DILL & YOGURT SAUCE

(Salmon-Spinach Patty pg. 174)

¼ cup Greek yogurt

½ lime (juice)

1 T fresh dill

¼ t Himalayan pink salt

¼ t garlic paste/minced garlic

In a bowl combine all ingredients. Store in an airtight container in the fridge for up to a week.

KALE PESTO SAUCE

(Zucchini Spaghetti pg. 171)

2 cups fresh kale

2 cups fresh basil

1 clove garlic

¼ cup pine nuts

¼ cup + 2 T extra virgin olive oil

¼ t Himalayan pink salt

Process all ingredients using a food processor or blender. Better when consumed the same day, but you can store in an airtight container in the fridge for a couple of days.

ASIATIC DRESSING

(Brussel Sprouts pg. 163)

¼ cup balsamic vinegar

2 T tamari sauce

2 T agave nectar

2 t sesame seeds

In a bowl combine all ingredients. Store in an airtight container in the fridge for up to 3 weeks.

WHITE TRUFFLE MARINADE

(Veggie Carpaccio pg. 146)

4 limes (juice)

1 T extra virgin olive oil

1 t white truffle oil

½ t agave nectar

½ t Himalayan pink salt

In a bowl combine all ingredients. Store in an airtight container in the fridge for up to a week.

VEGGIE CARPACCIO

SERVES 2-3

Maybe, like me, at some time during your pregnancy you won't be up for raw veggies that much. But trust me this is a yummy and fun recipe to make. It looks beautiful not only served at your table but will also look amazing when all those bright colors reach your system! It can be used as a starter (it's always great to start your main meals with a salad or something raw); you can also add a bed of greens and top with a poached egg to make it a meal. Remember cooking is all about getting creative!

1 peeled golden beet

1 peeled red beet

2 small zucchini

6 small radishes

¼ grapefruit

2 T sheep's milk feta cheese

1 T walnuts

2 T fresh mint

White Truffle Marinade
(pg. 145)

1. Using a mandoline or a sharp knife (please be careful with your fingers!! You'll be needing those too a lot!), very thinly slice veggies: zucchini into long thin slices and the beets and radishes into cute thin circles! (You can use any type of beets you like! Or other veggies too!)

2. Combine all ingredients for the marinade and toss the veggies with it (use a different bowl for red beets; otherwise it will turn all of the other veggies red!!).

3. Let the veggies marinate for at least 5 minutes (you can leave veggies in the marinade for up to a couple of days! That means you can use leftovers to add to a salad or sandwich!).

4. This is the really fun part, just like in art class! On a large plate start arranging the veggies, one layer of zucchini first and then get artsy with the remaining veggies!

5. Slice grapefruit into segments (no skin) and top off your
work of art with the grapefruit, walnuts, fresh mint and
feta cheese!

Veggie CARPACCIO

YOGURT MASSAGED KALE SALAD

SERVES 2

You don't know how much I love kale!! I could eat it for breakfast, lunch and dinner!!! In my smoothies, scrambled eggs, salads, soups, OMG! This is one of my favorite ways of eating it: raw and massaged! This causes the cellulose in the leaves to break down and the strong flavor, which usually scares people away from this deliciousness, is changed to a lighter one. A 2-3 minute massage will also make kale change its fibrous texture to a more silken, yummy one. (I know you are thinking that YOU are the one needing a massage! But trust me this is also relaxing! Plus you'll get a free hand moisturizing from the yogurt and oil!!). A quick tip for making salads is to include different textures and flavors to keep it fun and never get bored! Example: get the crunchy from nuts, popped quinoa or dry roasted chickpeas or grains; the sweetness from dried fruit or fruits such as goji and golden berries, strawberries and dates, the salty from feta cheese, olives, capers, etc.!

6 cups curly kale

¼ cup whole almonds / sliced

1 cup diced papaya

4 slices turkey bacon

Dressing

½ cup plain Greek yogurt

1 lemon (juice)

2 T extra virgin olive oil

1 t Himalayan pink salt

1. Cook turkey bacon in a skillet with no extra oil until crispy, for around 10 minutes (approx. 5 minutes per side). Slice it to the size you want or leave the strips whole if you prefer!

2. In a bowl whisk the Greek yogurt, lemon juice, extra virgin olive oil and salt.

3. With your hand remove kale stems (they can be a little woody in a raw salad); add the kale to the bowl with the dressing and start massaging the leaves with your hands for around 2-3 minutes (meanwhile you can visualize ocean waves or breathe deeply, and the relaxing effect will transfer to you too!).

4. Serve massaged kale leaves; top it off with the bacon, papaya and almonds!

YOGURT
Massaged *KALE*'s A LA D..

CHILLED BEET SOUP

SERVES 3

And for those days when all we can handle is soup but the temperature outside is wayyy too hot for warm soup, this Chilled Beet Soup is here to the rescue! It is so refreshing but at the same time fulfilling, loaded with vitamins and minerals from the beets and the bone broth! (You can do your own broth from the recipe that follows, or use a quality store-bought one, chicken or veggie, whichever you prefer or have at hand.) Cook this soup and keep it in the fridge for a week or freeze it for a month! Remember to never throw those beet leaves away, they are full of nutrients we need! Throw them into your green smoothie or sauté them with some garlic and onions! (These leaves get bad faster than the beets, so use them the day after you get them from the grocery store; beets can be used up through the following week!)

3 red beets

1 cup bone broth

2 T cashews

2 T apple cider vinegar

2 T plain Greek yogurt

2 stalks fresh dill or

1 T + more for garnish

6 stalks scallions or 1 T

1 clove garlic

½ t Himalayan pink salt

1 t sheep's milk feta crumbled for garnish

1. Add beets to a pot with water and bring to a boil. Let it simmer until beets are tender (see if you can easily pierce a knife through the center!).

2. Start peeling the beets with your hands (like rubbing the skin off; the skin will be so easy to remove that you won't need anything other than your hands!). Use a knife if it works better for you.

3. Add the cooked beets and the rest of the ingredients (except the cheese and extra dill which are used for garnish) to a blender and blend until smooth.

4. Transfer to a glass container and chill in the fridge for a couple of hours.

5. When it's nice and chilled serve in your favorite bowl with some sheep's milk feta on top if you are up to it and some more fresh dill!

Chilled BEET SOUP

MY MOMMY'S SOUP

MAKES 8 BOWLS

This soup gives you superpowers, believe me! For me it tastes just like heaven! (Especially when it's cooked by my mom.) It's packed with nutrients, minerals, protein and fiber!! I'll give you the recipe for the broth or stock, which can be cooked and saved for a week's reserve or frozen for months (this broth is a total lifesaver during your first trimester when you feel sick, because one can get all the minerals needed in a smooth way!). You can substitute the chicken for fish bones, roasted meat bones or just more veggies (the ones going bad in your fridge!) and use as a base for other soups or to cook brown rice, quinoa or other grains! I also need to tell you that this soup (whole version = broth + goodies) makes an excellent meal throughout the entire pregnancy (think second trimester protein needs too!), and also during breastfeeding. I had this soup at least three times a week during my postpartum period and I always say it was this soup that gave me superwoman or supermomma powers to survive those sleepless nights!

Bone Broth

1 whole chicken
½ onion, quartered
3 celery stalks, roughly chopped
2 carrots, roughly chopped
2 t ginger root, minced
2 t turmeric root, minced
1 T apple cider vinegar or white vinegar
1 clove of garlic
1 t whole peppercorns

1. Soak lentils overnight or for some hours so they are easier on your stomach.

2. Add all the "Bone Broth" ingredients to a pot; add water to cover them and cook for 3 hours to a whole day (you can get your hands busy as soon as you wake up; by lunch time your broth is ready!).

3. Strain the broth, discard the veggies and remove all the meat from the bones (wait a little for it to cool down so you don't burn your fingers! Also save the bones in a freezer bag to use for other stocks!).

4. Pour the broth into the pot again and add all the "Soup" ingredients but the kale. (We want that kale with some texture and color! So we add it at the end.

1 t Himalayan pink salt

5 stalks thyme or dill

Soup

1 cup quinoa

1 cup soaked lentils

1 carrot, sliced

½ cup edamame (no pods)

1 onion, chopped

1 bell pepper, chopped

1 corn on the cob kernels (makes ½ cup)

1 t ginger root, minced

1 t turmeric root, minced (or turmeric powder)

2 t Himalayan pink salt

2 cups sliced mushrooms

4 cups kale leaves

For the other veggies you can also use an organic veggie medley to save some time!)

5. Cook for around 20 minutes until lentils are cooked.

6. Turn off heat and add kale leaves (shredded into small pieces with your hands), and the shredded chicken meat. Check salt and you are ready to get boosted up!

MY MOMMY'S SOUP!

ROASTED CAULIFLOWER & TAHINI SOUP

SERVES 3-4

This soup is perfect when you want something creamy and comfy. It's so rich in flavors and nutrients that just one bowl will leave you ready to go! This recipe requires you to roast the cauliflower in the oven, so I encourage you to bake extra and use in other dishes such as pastas, cauliflower purée, or just tossed in a salad! I also call for broth; you can go ahead and cook your own broth (pg. 152) which will be just awesome for having those extra minerals and vitamins from the bone broth to nurture your growing baby. But again, as I mentioned earlier, if you are short of time look for a clean broth option in the supermarket. Remember to buy organic and again, I can't emphasize more: check ingredients (the list must look like a recipe with no weird, unpronounceable ingredients).

1 big cauliflower head (1.5 lbs. or 680 g)	1. Preheat oven to 425°F or 218°C.
2 T coconut oil	2. Toss the cauliflower (broken into florets), garlic and onion with the coconut oil and salt. Add to a baking dish and bake for 35 minutes.
2 cloves of garlic, whole	
½ onion, quartered	
1 t Himalayan pink salt	3. Let the cauliflower cool down a little before blending. (If you add very hot things into a blender it will explode and the splash will even reach your ceiling!)
½ cup tahini/sesame paste	
1 cup unsweetened full fat coconut milk	4. To your high speed blender (or just the one you have!) add the roasted cauliflower, garlic, onion, tahini paste, coconut milk and broth. Blend until smooth.
2 cups broth/stock	
	5. Check seasoning, add more salt if necessary and serve garnished with roasted cauliflower and fresh parsley!

ROASTED
Cauliflower &
TAHINI
SOUP

ASPARAGUS & CHICKPEA SOUP

SERVES 4

This soup will fully maintain you. You have the veggie quota in the asparagus and the protein in the chickpeas! I came up with this soup one day when I was looking for an ingredient to make my asparagus soup creamier, and there they were: some chickpea leftovers in my fridge!! And boom it was the perfect addition!! Here you can cook some extra chickpeas and eat them later with brown rice, add them to a fresh salad, stews or to try our finger-licking "Black Bean-Rosemary Hummus Crudité"!! (pg. 186). Remember that canned organic chickpeas with BPA-free lining can also be an option if you are in a hurry!

Approx 25 asparagus/ 250g / 9 oz

1 medium onion, chopped

1 small clean leek (optional), chopped

2 cloves garlic, minced

1 cup cooked chickpeas (I'll give you directions how to cook dried chickpeas)

1 cup water from asparagus or homemade stock/broth

1 T ghee/butter

1. Soak chickpeas overnight. If you forgot, just soak them in hot water for one hour. Drain water, add them to a pot, and cover them with water. Bring water to a boil, then lower heat to maintain a simmer and cook chickpeas until they are tender (for 1 lb. around 2 hours). Rinse chickpeas and save in an airtight container.

2. Trim the asparagus: the heads and the woody ends of the asparagus (a quick tip is to bend the asparagus until it breaks; it will break at the exact point, then use that asparagus as a guide to trim the others!).

3. Add those woody ends into a small pot with water (about 4 cups) and simmer for around 15 minutes. (While you wait, continue with the next steps. We are never wasting time! Remember you can also use any stock or broth you have at hand or a good quality store-bought!)

4. In a pan with 1 T ghee sauté the chopped onion, garlic and leek for around 5

minutes. Add the asparagus pieces including the heads and sauté
for 3 minutes (we need them bright green, crisp and tender
so no overcooking!).

5. Take out some
asparagus heads to
use as garnish.
Add the
rest of the
asparagus,
onion, leeks,
garlic,
cooked
chickpeas,
and stock
to a blender
and blend until
smooth; adjust salt
if needed.

6. Serve and garnish with
some whole chickpeas and
asparagus heads, drizzle some extra
virgin olive oil and enjoy!!

Asparagus &
Chickpea soup

COLLARD GREEN
Salmon Wrap

w/ Miso +
Peanut Dipping
Sauce

COLLARD GREEN SALMON WRAP
(W/ MISO & PEANUT DIPPING SAUCE)

SERVES 2

There is this thing about eating my food with my hands - I just love it! You can get more engaged with your meal and maybe make a little mess (which is cool too; we need those moments of imperfection to free our heads a little from trying to always be so perfect! At least it works for me!). The collard green tortilla is such a great substitute for a flour tortilla. You can make this for dinner and then use those extra collard green leaves to wrap up some scrambled eggs or an omelette the next morning! Or they can be the stars in your next "make your own burrito" party. (If you need a quick wrap you can always go for a sushi nori sheet!! I actually use those to wrap up everything! Of course, I gave you the collard green recipe because I wanted you to have it, but please do have this option in the back of your mind always!) Also this Miso & Peanut Dipping Sauce works wonderfully in fresh salads, tossed with some baked eggplant or to dip some raw organic broccoli!

Collard greens leaves (1 per wrap)
1 cup arugula or watercress
1 cup mushrooms, sliced
2 stalk scallions, sliced
½ clove garlic, minced
2 fresh wild salmon fillets (each the size of your palm)
1 T white miso paste
1 cup quinoa soaked or washed
1 Hass avocado, ripe
Miso and Peanut Dipping Sauce (recipe pg. 142)

Collard leaves

1. With a knife remove the collard green stem (all the way from the leaf's spine, kind of shaving the stem so the entire leaf is the same thickness!).

2. Bring a pot to a boil, add the leaves and boil for 2 minutes.

3. Take them out and immediately run under cold water to stop the cooking (we want them bright green!).

4. Dry each leaf with a paper towel and you are ready to make some wraps! (You can save them in an airtight container with a paper towel in between the leaves for up to 3 days!)

Quinoa

1. Soak quinoa from the night before or if you forgot just wash it thoroughly before cooking (this will remove saponin, which is a coating quinoa has that can alter taste!).

2. Cook quinoa with water, stock or broth if you have at hand! The measurement is 1 cup of dry quinoa for 2 cups of liquid!! (Remember that you can cook extra to transform into other dishes such as salads or porridges, or just to scramble some eggs with it! Hubby loves that; it's a healthier version of a Colombian "Scrambled eggs with rice.")

3. Cook until all liquid is absorbed and season accordingly! (It's better to save leftovers unseasoned so you can sauté them with some onion, garlic, spices and fresh herbs when ready to use.)

Salmon

1. Season salmon with Himalayan pink salt, garlic, scallions and miso paste; let it marinade for at least 5 minutes in the fridge.

2. In a very hot pan, melt 1 t of coconut oil or avocado oil and add the salmon skin-side down. Sear for 5 minutes or until skin is crispy brown. Turn salmon and cook for another 3-4 minutes, until it feels tender to the touch (stick out your finger and feel it!).

Mushrooms

1. Slice mushrooms and cook with sliced scallions in a heated pan with 1 t of ghee, add some salt and stir until golden brown.

Putting everything together:

Form your wrap by placing the leaf on a plate, spreading some of the "**Miso and Peanut Dipping Sauce**" (pg. 142) on top, adding arugula, watercress or any leafy green you want, and then some quinoa, mushrooms, the salmon and some sliced avocado. Roll into a wrap! Serve with extra Miso and Peanut Dipping Sauce on the side!

ALMOND & AMARANTH CRUSTED FISH SANDWICH (W/ BRUSSEL SPROUTS)

SERVES 2

I'm a total fish sandwich fan, but as we all know it is not very easy to find clean and healthy versions out there. Luckily the scarcity of better options for my favorites in restaurants just encourages my inner chef soul to experiment with them at home. (You'll call me crazy but I even do healthy copycat versions of dishes I love from restaurants!! These brussels sprouts are a clear example.) The amaranth and almond breading was originally used for my star chicken sandwich, but during pregnancy I experimented one day with fish and OMG it was just magical (you can also try using shrimp!! Think healthy rock shrimp! You can also pair it with my homemade Honey Mustard). This healthier and gluten-free breading is not only full of nutrients, but it gives an extra crunchiness that combined with my Honey Mustard is simply a party in your mouth. This brussels sprouts recipe, on the other hand, was born when I found out that my favorite brussels sprouts dish from that restaurant I loved were pan-fried with canola oil (OMG), and that wasn't something I wanted to eat that often! So I came up with this recipe. They are baked using coconut oil and the sauce is made with tamari (instead of soy sauce) and with agave (instead of white sugar!). Enjoy!

2 corvina fillets (the size of your palm)	**Crusted Fish Sandwich**
1 egg	1. Preheat oven to 450°F or 230°C.
½ garlic clove, minced	
1 t Himalayan pink salt	2. In a bowl whisk eggs, salt, pepper, paprika, minced garlic and oregano leaves.
1 t pepper	Add the fish fillets and let them marinate in the fridge for at least 5 minutes.
1 t paprika	
1 T fresh oregano leaves	3. On a wide plate sprinkle the amaranth and almond flour. Then take the fish fillets and cover them with the almond & amaranth mixture, making sure the entire fillet is covered by it! Chill in the fridge for another 5 minutes so the breading really sticks to the fish.

¼ cup almond meal/almond flour
¼ cup dry amaranth
4 slices of sprouted grain bread or
artisan whole wheat bread
Sliced pickles
Romaine lettuce or any leafy green
Honey Mustard
(Recipe on pg.143)

2 lbs. brussels sprouts
½ t Himalayan pink salt
¼ cup coconut oil
Asiatic Marinade
(Recipe on pg.145)

4. Bake fish on top of a roasting rack so all sides get crispy. (Just think about the roaster pan you use for your turkey on Thanksgiving but with the roasting rack upside down. The idea is that the fish gets elevated from the bottom of the pan so the breading cooks nicely from every angle!!) Bake for 10-15 minutes or until you see the breading crispy!

Brussel Sprouts with Asiatic Dressing

1. Preheat oven to 450°F or 230°C.

2. Trim ends of brussels sprouts, then halve lengthwise (remember to discard any yellow leaf).

3. Rub the brussels sprouts with coconut oil and salt. Bake on a sheet pan (use a silicon mat or baking paper underneath for better results). Bake for 40-45 minutes and with a wooden spoon toss them around every 10 minutes until you see beautiful dark crispy outer leaves!

4. Add brussels sprouts to a bowl with all the ingredients from the Asiatic Dressing (pg. 145), toss a little with your hands and serve!

Let's put everything together:

Toast bread, spread a generous amount of our heavenly Honey Mustard (pg. 143), add some greens (butter lettuce, arugula, romaine or just your favorite leafy green!), and then our perfectly crusted baked fish and some pickles. Serve with a bowl of brussels sprouts on the side!

with
* * *
* BRUSSEL
* SPROUTS *
*

· Almond & Amaranth crusted. · FISH SANDWICH .

TURMERIC SHRIMP STUFFED PORTOBELLO MUSHROOMS

SERVES 2

Being in the "sandwich" mood, let me tell you that portobello mushrooms are great substitutes for buns! They are commonly used for healthy burgers (which are yummy!), but I wanted something different yet simple, so I tried filling them with shrimp, my beloved avocado and some greens, and yumms yumms!! Have in mind that you can bake extra mushrooms and stuff them with quinoa or rice, use as patty for a veggie burger, slice them into your salad, or simply eat them whole as a side dish! I love mushrooms because they go perfectly with everything! Plus portobello mushrooms have a firm texture that can trick some for meat!! (Think using portobello in a lasagna, in between some sprouted grain buns or sliced as "carnitas" in a taco!) The key is in the seasoning because they are like sponges! They absorb all the flavors!

4 whole portobello mushrooms	**Mushrooms**
½ cup extra virgin olive oil	
2 cloves garlic, sliced	1. Preheat oven to 450°F or 230°C.
4 stalks thyme	
2 stalks scallions, sliced	2. In a bowl combine olive oil, chopped scallions, sliced garlic and salt. On a
½ t Himalayan pink salt	baking sheet (covered with baking paper or silicone mat), place mushrooms with the stem side up and pour the olive oil mixture on top. Add the fresh thyme on top (you can use rosemary or fresh oregano, whatever you have at hand!).
	3. Bake for approximately 15 minutes until you see them moist and dark in color!
8-10 wild shrimp	**Shrimp**
(depending on the size)	
2 t turmeric powder	1. In a bowl season the cleaned shrimp with turmeric, pepper, curry and minced

½ t ground pepper

1 t curry

½ clove garlic, minced

1 t ghee / coconut oil / red palm oil

2 cups of fresh watercress or arugula

garlic (I leave the shell on my wild shrimp because it gets so crunchy! Plus it's fiber, and we need lots of that! Of course if you don't like it remove it).

2. To a hot pan add red palm oil and shrimp. Cook for 2 minutes per side. Remember it is very important to buy wild shrimp and it's better if they are frozen. Those you see fresh in the grocery store have usually been previously thawed (it is not good to freeze, thaw and refreeze!!). If you can, make sure they are really fresh and then buy them that way! And it is even better when they are local!

Let's put everything together:

1. Make a bed of greens on a plate. You can use arugula, watercress or your favorite leafy green! (tossed with 1 t of olive oil or homemade dressing if you prefer).

2. Use portobello caps as your buns; fill them with sliced avocado and your perfectly pan- seared shrimp!

Turmeric Shrimp STUFFED PORTOBELLO Mushrooms

GReeN chicken Salad

STUFFED BUTTERNUT SQUASH

GREEN CHICKEN SALAD STUFFED BUTTERNUT SQUASH

SERVES 4

I remember when I was little I loved a chicken salad my mom bought at the grocery store when we came on vacation to the US. It was heaven for me; it had marshmallows in it!! Imagine how healthy it was OMG. So I grew up loving chicken and tuna salads, but again, it's difficult to eat a healthy one out there; most of them are made with mayo full of nasty ingredients, etc. So, I experimented with better ingredients like avocado and Greek yogurt to get that creaminess we all love from chicken salads (you can use a good canned tuna too!!). Besides having it inside the squash, I love this salad in between bread for a sandwich, on top of massaged kale, to make lettuce wraps, or to mix with lentil pasta for a cold salad! (Again, we have infinite options here!!!) Additionally, this baked butternut squash is simply de-li-cious and so easy to make!! Please do bake extra so you can blend it into a soup or a purée, eat as a side dish, or stuff with ground turkey, quinoa, OMG sooo many options!!

½ butternut squash per person

2 T coconut oil

1 t Himalayan pink salt

Butternut squash

1. Preheat oven to 450°F or 230°C.

2. Cut the butternut squash in half and remove the seeds. (I normally leave the skin on because it gets roasted and yummy, but for some people, it can feel a little fibrous. So it's up to you if you peel it or not! You can also leave the skin on and then eat just the inside meat and leave the skin!)

3. Rub the squash with the coconut oil and pink salt, place on a baking sheet and roast for 15-20 minutes. (Insert a chopstick in the middle to feel if it's tender; that's when it's ready!)

400 g chicken breast/3 cups
shredded chicken
4 broccoli heads
1 ripe avocado
2 limes (juice)
¼ cup plain Greek yogurt
½ t Himalayan pink salt

Chicken Salad

1. Add chicken breasts to a pot with water and a little salt, and bring it to a boil. Check if chicken is cooked (with a knife cut open the center of the breast a little, the insides should be white, not pink). Save that water for extra flavor when cooking quinoa or brown rice! Or as a stock base for a soup!

2. Let the chicken cool down a little bit in the bowl before shredding. I love shredding it with my fingers; they work better than forks!

3. Cut off the very ends of the broccoli florets and save the stalks and other smaller pieces to make a broccoli soup! (I love using the stalks for stocks, just remember to remove the woody parts with a vegetable peeler!)

4. In a bowl whisk the Greek yogurt, ripe avocado (mashed), lime juice and salt (the avocado must "melt" into a type of avocado mayo!). Add the raw broccoli florets and shredded chicken and mix with your hands! (Or with a spoon; I love using my hands, sorry for the mess.) Make sure everything is covered by the "avo-mayo".

Let's put everything together:

Serve half a squash per person (if it's medium to small size, if it's too large cut it in half again!); stuff with the chicken salad and enjoy!!!

BOCCONCINI STUFFED TURKEY MEATBALLS (ZUCCHINI SPAGHETTI WITH KALE PESTO)

SERVES 4-6

This is where I cannot say no to cheese nevaaaa. I'm sorry but I love my turkey balls filled with cheese (especially bufala bocconcini, a fresh, soft, and mild cheese. Buy imported!!!); they are the very best! When I was moving from Atlanta to Miami in college, my dad flew from Colombia to help me drive my U-Haul. The only thing I had left was ground turkey so I cooked like a 100 mini turkey balls filled with cheese, and that was all we ate for 9 hours straight and for the following two days in Miami (OMG we ate them like popcorn). So every time I cook them my dad tells the story (nice memories! Makes me feel old!). Back on topic, the Kale Pesto Sauce is another favorite (of course this book is filled with favorites, duh). I use it in salads, pastas, spread on rice cakes with mozzarella and tomato, as a marinade for chicken or veggies... countless options. You can make a little more and save it in a jar in the fridge for a couple of days!! So just imagine the turkey balls, Kale Pesto Sauce and the freshness of the raw zucchini pasta in one killer bite! Amazing.

785 g ground turkey/3 cups
1 T paprika
½ T mustard powder
2 T whole grain mustard
1 T yellow mustard
½ clove garlic, minced
½ medium onion, finely chopped
2 stalks fresh rosemary, chopped
¼ almond meal/flour
Bocconcini cheese balls
(1 per meatball)
1 zucchini per person
Kale Pesto Sauce (Recipe pg. 144)

Meatballs

1. In a bowl combine chopped fresh rosemary, minced garlic, chopped onion, mustards, paprika, almond flour and ground turkey; mix with your hands. If you need more consistency add a little more almond flour! (You can also use flax meal; it's just for binding.) You can season meat hours before for extra flavor.

2. Place a bocconcini ball in your hand and start covering it with the seasoned ground turkey until you form the meatball (if you want to premake some, an awesome tip is to freeze the meatballs arranged on a baking sheet, and when frozen transfer them to a freezer bag or airtight container! When you are ready to eat them, pop them in the oven! Or thaw overnight in the fridge!) You can also use this mixture for patties or to stuff peppers and zucchinis, or for eggplant lasagnas and casseroles!

171

Zucchini Spaghetti

1. If you have a veggie spiralizer, great! Wash your organic zucchini and just run it through the spiralizer! You can also use a mandoline with the julienne blade or a julienne peeler, or go back to basics and cut those long skinny strips with a sharp knife! (I use one zucchini per person but you can use more - even more veggies, yay!! It depends on the size of your zucchini.) If you want to go for a greater pasta effect use a sprouted grain or bean pasta instead!

Let's put everything together:

In a bowl toss the Kale Pesto Sauce (pg. 144), zucchini pasta and meatballs, and serve on your favorite plate, sprinkling some crushed red pepper to finish. You can have a slice of sprouted grain bread to mop up all the yumminess left on the plate!

uFFED TURKEY MEATBALLS

(zucchini SPAGHETTI with KALE PESTO)

SALMON-SPINACH PATTY + MASHED SWEET POTATO

SERVES 4

I know you'll be thinking that I must be a little out of my mind because burgers go with french fries not mashed potato. But all we pregnants know there is something about weird combinations that we really love, and I really enjoyed the smoothness and sweetness of the mashed potato with the salty, buttery flavors of the salmon patty! Yumm!! This salmon patty is an all-in-one combo for greens, protein, and good fats! Just what we love! (You can make extra and freeze for later!) About this healthy mashed sweet potato (where yogurt gives it the creaminess component) - it could be a perfect Thanksgiving side dish, part of a terrine (think a layer of mashed potato, then sautéed greens and a seared fish on top!), or maybe a type of Peruvian causa (layered mashed potato with our Green Chicken Salad (pg. 169)).

But, if you really want to go the traditional way of burger and fries, just preheat your oven to 450°F or 230°C, slice sweet potato into french fries, toss with some coconut oil, Himalayan pink salt, paprika and fresh thyme and bake for 25 minutes until brown. There you have your **Baked Sweet Potato Fries!**

500 g/1 lb. salmon	**Salmon patty**
(3 filets the size of your palm)	
1 T plain Greek yogurt/sour cream	1. Add all the ingredients except the salmon to a food processor and blend until ev-
2 T yellow mustard	erything is finely chopped. Then add the salmon (no skin) and pulse until chopped.
1 clove garlic	Try not to overdo it so it doesn't turn into a purée; we want some texture! (Also, I
3 cups spinach	need to tell you that if you make this exact mixture using cooked salmon and a little
2 stalks scallions	more yogurt you'll get a nice salmon spread! OMG delicious!!!)
1 t Himalayan pink salt	
2 T coconut oil/ghee	2. Form patties the size you want and cook in a pan over medium heat with ghee
Butter lettuce leaves	or coconut oil. Cook 4 minutes per side (you'll see a nice golden brown!).
Cucumber slices	

Dill & Yogurt Sauce (pg, 144)

2 medium sweet potatoes
2 T sour cream or Greek yogurt
2 T chicken or veggie stock
(optional)
4 stalks fresh parsley
1 t Himalayan pink salt

Mashed Sweet Potato

1. In a pot bring water with a little salt to a boil and add the potatoes (peeled and cut into chunks). Cook until tender for about 20 minutes. (You can also bake the whole potatoes, pierced with a fork at 400°F or 204°C for 45 minutes, then peel skin off.)

2. Mash the potatoes until smooth, then add the chopped parsley, sour cream (or plain Greek yogurt or some coconut milk!) and stock if you have at hand! The stock will enhance the flavors sooo much! Add salt at the end because the stock adds some more and we don't want to overdo it!

Let's put everything together:

Spread some Dill & Yogurt Sauce (pg. 144) on top of the patty, top with cucumber slices and wrap in butter lettuce leaves. Serve with some mashed potatoes on the side! (You can add a forkful of mashed potatoes to every burger bite like I do!!!)

SALMON - SPINACH PATTY
+ mashed sweet potato

BLACK BEANS & BROWN RICE

SERVES 4-5

My mom and dad grew up eating rice and beans every day for breakfast and dinner!! No wonder they grew up to be extremely healthy adults! (It's still too heavy for me to think about having beans that early and that late in the day.) However, beans have had a piece of my heart since I was a kid. My grandma's red kidney beans with green plantains and fried egg are absolutely the best in the world!! But after living several years in Miami the Cuban influence has made me switch to black beans as my favorite type of beans! I love my black beans and rice - they make the perfect plant-based meal; plus it's extremely cheap and you always have them in your pantry! That's why this pairing has been around forever in so many different cultures. It's important to have several things in mind with this recipe: you must soak your beans to make them more digestible and smoother! (Especially now that your pregnant stomach suffers more!!!) You can actually soak them for several days in the fridge to really make them smooth. If you're feeling energetic, cook in bulk and transform into other dishes (or freeze!!!). You can blend into a soup with some stock, form a patty adding eggs and some almond meal, toss cold into a salad, use in tacos or just save leftovers to crack some eggs on top (that's what we called in Colombia "calentado": rice, beans and eggs! The bomb).

Beans

2 cups black beans
1 T apple cider vinegar
2 bay leaves
1 t cumin
2 carrots
1 medium onion, chopped
2 stalks scallions, chopped
1 clove garlic, minced

1. Soak black beans with just enough water to cover them overnight. This is crucial to do with black beans so they are less heavy (plus they cook faster).

2. Rinse black beans and place with enough water to cover them in a medium sauce pan. Add the bay leaf and bring to a boil. (Do not add salt at this point or they will take longer to cook!!!)

3. Lower temperature and add the whole carrots; let beans simmer, stirring

1 T coconut oil

1 t Himalayan pink salt

1 ripe avocado

1 ripe sweet plantain (completely black skinned! Yes! That ripe.)

Fresh parsley for garnish

½ cup stock (optional)

occasionally. Check beans and add more water when you see the liquid level lowering. Continue adding more water to cover beans until tender (around 5-7 cups more! You'll see! No big deal, just keep adding liquid until completely tender!!). Simmer for approximately one hour!

4. Meanwhile, in a skillet with coconut oil sauté onion, chives, garlic, cumin and salt for around 7 minutes until onions are soft and brown.

5. Add the onion mixture, cooked whole carrots, ¼ cup of cooked lentils and ½ cup of stock or some of the liquid left from the beans into a blender and blend until smooth.

6. Add this liquid and the apple cider vinegar to the cooked beans. Stir and check seasoning!! (Tip: if you want your black beans soupier add more stock to that blender; if you want them creamier add some more cooked beans to that same mixture to blend!)

2 cups brown rice

1 cup water

1 cup stock

Brown Rice

1. Rinse brown rice under running water until the water is clear.

2. In a pot bring rice, water and stock or just water to a boil. (Remember my tip about using leftovers for sweet recipes such as our Brown Rice Porridge (pg. 128); in that case you want the rice unseasoned!). If you are using the rice just for savory dishes I recommend using stock or broth (homemade (pg. 152) or clean store-bought option); it gives much more flavor to the rice!

3. Let it simmer until rice is tender! Add salt according to taste!

Sweet Plantains

1. Cut plantain (must have skin completely black= super ripe!) in cubes and sauté with 1 t of coconut oil until golden brown!! (Yummsss, this is my favorite.)

Let's put everything together

You can serve beans and rice side by side or mix them together! Top off with some avocado, sweet plantains and fresh parsley! I like having a bed of leafy greens underneath so I can mix everything together! I love the fresh greens with warm beans, a party of flavors and textures!

❀ Black Beans & BROWN RICE ❀

COCONUT CURRIED LENTILS & QUINOA

SERVES 4-6

Lentils are my favorite non-vegetable protein ever! I grew up eating lots of lentils, and of course lentils at my parents' house taste like heaven to me!! Without discrediting mine because they are actually pretty yummy, let me tell you! I'm in love with this recipe because it's not only incredibly yummy, but easy to cook, serve and eat, as well as to cook in bulk and freeze and then save my life when I don't have an idea what to cook!!! (Yes, that happens to me too!! Like when I'm back from a get-away weekend and haven't planned anything, or my pregnant body is just too tired.) Give them a try! They make a perfect lunch or dinner!

2 cups brown lentils (or your favorite kind!)	1. Soak lentils and quinoa (in separate bowls) overnight. It's very important to soak lentils to make them more digestible. Quinoa is just fine with a good rinse! Discard the soaking water.
2 cups quinoa	
4 cups stock	
1 can whole coconut milk	2. In a saucepan heat coconut oil, then add chopped onion, minced garlic, minced ginger and bay leaf and cook for 5 minutes.
1 onion, chopped	
4 cloves of garlic, minced	
1 T ginger root, minced	3. Add the turmeric (remember to use turmeric and pepper together to potentialize turmeric's anti-inflammatory powers!), pepper, salt, curry and cumin to the onion mixture. Cook for a minute and enjoy the amazing dance of smells that won't leave your kitchen for a couple of hours!
2 T curry powder	
2 T turmeric powder	
1 t cumin powder	
1 bay leaf	
½ t pepper	4. Add soaked lentils, quinoa, stock and coconut milk. Have in mind that you can use any stock you have at hand! Veggie or chicken from other soup recipes or as I've been saying: if the ingredient list qualifies, organic store-bought could be an option too!! If not just use water!
1 t Himalayan pink salt	
½ cup Greek yogurt (optional)	
1 T coconut oil	
Fresh parsley to garnish	

5. As soon as it reaches a boil, add the spinach (or you can also use kale, collard greens...) and let the lentils simmer for around 25 minutes until they are tender! (Try one and check, don't overcook, otherwise you'll have a lentil purée!)

6. Serve in a cute bowl, add some Greek yogurt if you want (for me it's a must, it just balances the curry flavors so nicely!), and top it off with fresh parsley!

7. If you are freezing half your portion, let it cool down and then store in a glass airtight container and freeze for up to a month! (I recommend that if you plan to freeze, just omit the spinach and add it fresh when reheating! Spinach is one of those foods you don't want to reheat that much!)

= Coconut = curried lentils &
QUINOA

snacks, bi

es & more

Here we have from easy-as-pie (organic pie please) sweet bites and baked goodies to some must-have-handy snacks! Remember that pregnancy makes us hungry! And it's easier to prevent nausea, tiredness or grumpiness if you just SNACK! Smart snacking also keeps our blood sugar steady! (AKA our baby's blood sugar will stay regulated!!! He can't do it on his own!) But we just don't want any granola bar for a snack, full of GMOs, oils, refined flours and sugars! We want real snacks that boost us and our baby the right way!

Most of the following recipes can be made as a batch and saved for you to have handy whenever your hungry baby attacks! Remember it's always a matter of being prepared, so let's go for it!

BLACK BEAN-ROSEMARY HUMMUS CRUDITÉ

This is so perfect to have at hand. It will save your life by feeding unexpected visitors, letting you snack at home, or being so versatile to take on the go! You can use leftover cooked chickpeas and black beans from other recipes, or use organic BPA-free canned versions if it's easier for you! You can use your favorite veggies to dip! But if you don't feel like eating raw veggies, thin rice cakes (broken in half) work just perfectly too!! (Or pita chips and crackers with nice ingredients! Remember all we've learnt from the "Reading Labels & Shopping Tips" section.) You can make a batch and save in the fridge for up to a week or in the freezer for about 7 months!!

1 cup cooked chickpeas

1 cup cooked black beans

4 T tahini/sesame paste

2 cloves garlic

1 T extra virgin olive oil

2 limes (juice)

6 T fresh rosemary

¼ t Himalayan pink salt

⅛ t paprika

Fresh veggies:
I use bell peppers, radishes, endives, cucumber and carrots

1. If you are cooking grains from scratch look for chickpea recipe (pg. 156) and black beans (pg. 178).

2. If you are using some leftovers or canned versions, discard liquid first and then add all ingredients to a food processor or blender and blend until smooth.

3. Cut bell peppers and carrots into sticks, slice radishes and separate endive leaves.

4. Serve hummus in your favorite bowl, garnish with some extra chickpeas and rosemary, and drizzle some olive oil and paprika on top. To finish your masterpiece, arrange veggies around a dish in a pretty way and enjoy!

Black Bean-Rosemary Hummus crudité ♡

SPICED POPCORN!

SPICED POPCORN

I can bet the number of movies you've watched will peak during these 9 months! You'll see how easily you'll change a dinner night or party for homemade food and movies! (One of my favorite plans even before pregnancy!) So of course we hate those microwave popcorn bags; they are so full of s****. The bag is made up of perfluorooctanoic acid (PFOA), a chemical that causes infertility and cancer, and the contents go from partially hydrogenated soybean oil, propyl galate (linked to breathing and stomach problems and skin rashes, among other issues) to TBHQ (linked to asthma, ADHD in children, allergies and dermatitis, among others). So let's save ourselves some problems and make our own! It's so easy and way better tasting!

If you don't have a hot air popcorn maker (which I strongly recommend! It's a great buy, especially if you like to snack on popcorn or watch lots of movies! It literally pops corn with just hot air, no oil needed!!), you can go old school and just combine ½ cup of popcorn kernels with 1 T of red palm oil or coconut oil in a pot, put the lid on and let it pop!!!

-Turmeric & cheese (½ cup popcorn kernels + 2 t melted ghee + 2 t turmeric + ¼ t Himalayan pink salt + grated hard cheese to taste!)

-Honey & sesame seeds (½ cup popcorn kernels + 2 T raw unfiltered honey/maple syrup + 2 T black sesame seeds)

-Ghee (½ cup popcorn kernels + 2 ½ t melted ghee + ¼ t Himalayan pink salt)

STEAMED ARTICHOKES

I could sit down and eat 10 artichokes in a row! They are so yummy, nutritious, and also make the perfect snack! Let's say it's a more elaborate snack which requires more time to make, especially when you feel like you need to snack ASAP before killing someone!! So whenever you feel encouraged just cook some extra and store in the fridge for up to 5 days! Get creative with the dipping area, I love ghee with turmeric because it's simple and good, but you can try any of the sauces from "To Use as a Dressing, Spread or Dip!" (pg. 140); just be creative!

Whole artichokes

1 lemon (juice)

1 T ghee

½ t turmeric

¼ t pepper

1. With a good knife cut the stems an inch from the top of the artichoke.

2. Place artichokes in water with lemon juice to prevent the artichokes from oxidizing. (It's not such a big deal; it's only for the artichoke to keep its nice green color!)

3. In a pot bring water to a boil and cook artichokes tops up for 30 minutes.

4. Combine melted ghee, turmeric and pepper in a sauce bowl.

5. Just in case you need it... Eating an artichoke 101:
- Start eating the outer leaves by dipping the flesh ends in the ghee and scraping the meat with your teeth.
- Eat all the leaves until you reach the hairy center (an inedible part protecting the artichoke heart).
- Scrape the "hairs" with a spoon, and there you have it!!! The super yummy artichoke heart!!! If you really love the person you are sharing an artichoke with, you'll let them eat the heart (or just don't share your artichoke so you have it all for yourself!).

STEAMED
ARTICHOKES!

THE PERFECT KALE CHIPS

As you may already know I do really love kale in all its forms, and this is a yummy one too! I experimented a lot with this recipe because I really wanted to get to a crunchy kale chip, as crunchy as a real chip! (There you go; if you crave chips, go for these!!) So you'll find all the tips for the perfect kale chip here! Of course you can bake a batch and save in an airtight container to keep on a counter for weeks! So give this one a try! This recipe is close to my heart because I shared it in a video on my friend's YouTube channel (we had so much fun!).

4 cups fresh kale (I used curly but you can use your favorite kind!)

2 T coconut oil

1 t turmeric powder

1 t ginger powder

1 t paprika

½ t pepper

½ t garlic powder

½ t onion powder

¼ t cayenne pepper

1 lemon zest

½ t Himalayan pink salt

1. Preheat oven to 350°F or 177°C.

2. Wash and dry kale leaves with paper towels (the drying is crucial for the crunchiness of the chip as the water will become steam in the oven, making them soggy).

3. With your hands remove stems and cut kale leaves into chip size.

4. In a bowl combine the coconut oil, spices and salt (you can use the spices you want! Experiment with your favorites!). Add kale and with your hands rub the leaves with the oil and spices. (I know I love getting my hands dirty, but they are the best kitchen tools ever!)

5. Spread leaves on a baking sheet using a silicon mat or baking paper underneath. Distribute the kale evenly making sure to separate one piece from the other (this space between them is the second most crucial element to ensure those chips are nice and crispy!).

6. Bake for 15 minutes, turn baking sheet around and let them bake from the other side another 15 minutes.

The Perfect ♥ KALE CHiPS!

7. Take them out, let them cool down a little (if you can resist eating the whole thing right away), and enjoy!

8. After they are at room temperature you can store in an airtight container to leave out on the counter for up to two weeks!!

Walnut

Goat
cheese

Filled
Dates

Peanut
Butter +
Goji Berries

FILLED DATES

Dates became my go-to dessert when I needed something fast!
(Plus dates are great for digestion! And lots of other health benefits!) I used to have my dates filled with nuts and nut butter
only, but then I saw dates filled with cheese on a trip to Europe.
I gave it a try, and it's sooo good; the perfect balance of sweet
and salty! You can use your favorite dried fruit instead of dates
too! Dried figs or prunes stuffed with cashew, almond or peanut
butters, or the actual nuts!

FRUIT TOSSED WITH SUPER GOODIES

As I've mentioned before, I can really be sneaky when talking about superfoods and other healthy goodies like seeds. I came up with this tossed fruit one morning when hubs was in a hurry and was heading out with a banana in his hand when I stopped him. A banana is definitely not breakfast! In regular "in a hurry" situations I make him a green smoothie, but there was no time for that!! So I just chopped half a banana and half an apple and started throwing things into a bowl like crazy!! Try it with your favorite fruits and powdered superfoods!! (I usually eat ½ banana in one sitting; as I've mentioned before, fruit is great!! But it has sugar too!!) After that morning this became part of my speedy snacks repertoire!! (And sometimes breakfast when I add sprouted grain toast underneath my tossed fruit!!)

Your favorite fruit (apple, banana, pineapple, pear, mango) in small chunks

1 T peanut butter

1 t powdered moringa leaf

1 t powdered spirulina

1 t chia seeds

1 t hemp seeds

1 t flax seeds

Toss everything in a bowl using your hands and ta-da! Eat immediately with your hands so you can lick all that goodness from your fingers! If you want to skip the peanut butter add ½ lemon (juice)!

Fruit Tossed with SUPER Goodies ☆

RICE CRACKERS

Brown rice crackers are my very best friends when it comes to snacking; they are made of simple, good ingredients and are a total white canvas! They go perfectly with sweet and savory toppings, so let your imagination fly!!! (If you are a cracker lover, read the ingredient list on the box and switch to brown rice crackers now!) I will give you some ideas on some toppings. Honestly, their versatility saves my life when I need a quick breakfast too! (For breakfast I love having one savory topped with an egg, and another one sweet topped with fruit or nut butters!)

PRUNE PRESERVE + cottage cheese + MINT

Peanut Butter

rice crackers

AV♥CAD♥
+ HEMP SEEDS
+ GOJI
 BERRIES

COCOA NIBS

Banana + COCOA NIBS

GOAT CHEESE +
walnuts +
ROSEMARY +
HONEY

DIY TRAIL MIX

You may think I just like making my life difficult by also mixing my own trail mix. (Right? Since they sell all types of trail mixes ready to open and eat!) But trust me, I loveee to be efficient with my time and the extra 2 minutes it takes to make this trail mix will be so worth it for you too if you read the ingredient lists of the trail mixes out there: sulfur dioxide to preserve dried fruit, citric acid, nuts roasted in GMOs and refined oils like soybean oil and sunflower oil, among other nasty and unnecessary ingredients! I feel bad when I see people with their trail mix bags thinking they are snacking right because sadly they are not; they are eating masked garbage! So let's give it a try; it's way too easy not to do it! I premake a lot and store in huge mason jars!! It's a great idea to always carry a bag of these in your purse or in your car! Mommas-to-be need to be prepared for when hunger attacks!

Buy unroasted versions of your nuts, unless they are roasted with a healthy oil (or just roast them yourself! Just add them to a hot pan and stir constantly for 5 minutes; if you want more flavor add a t of ghee, some paprika and fresh rosemary to the pan!!!). I'll give you my basic trail mix recipe but you can come up with your own signature trail mix. Add your favorite nuts, dried fruit and maybe some raw cacao nibs or unsweetened chocolate chips! (I add 1 cup of each nut and ½ cup for dried fruits and extras!)

200

DIY
TRAIL MIX

CASHEWS

Almonds

Pistachios

...nuts

...uts

Mulberries

Golden
Berries

GOJI
BERRIES

PINEAPPLE- COCONUT
ICE
CREAM

PINEAPPLE-COCONUT ICE CREAM

SERVES 2

I'm not such an ice cream fan, but whenever I feel like having some I grab my super blender and throw these simple in-gredients in! It's so simple yet yummy!! No need for an ice cream machine. You can change pineapple for your favorite fruit (it needs to be frozen!), and again you can go crazy with toppings here! Another combination I love is pineapple and rosemary with some cacao nibs and chia seeds sprinkled on top, yuuummm! Remember you need to eat immediately, or save in an airtight container in the freezer for months! (Just let it thaw for around 3 minutes before eating!) For those yogurt ice cream lovers out there, this is a wayyy better option! No hidden ingredients but only real ones! Just use plain yogurt (no extra sugars) instead of coconut milk!!

2 cups frozen pineapple

1 cup whole fat coconut milk

2 T raw unfiltered honey

4 T fresh mint + some for garnish

Toasted coconut

Place ingredients in a blender, blend until smooth (you'll have to stop the blend-er and scrape everything down with a spatula and blend again, until completely smooth), serve and garnish with toasted coconut and mint and eat immediately! It's that simple!

CHOCOAVOCADO MOUSSE

SERVES 2-3

As a declared chocoholic I'm always looking for smart ways to get my doses. During pregnancy this can easily become one of your favorite treats! It gives you the smoothness and sweetness of a real mousse but from real nutrient-dense sources! Yay! Just what we need for our growing bean! Plus it's easyyy to do!! I sometimes have this as a breakfast with some of my DIY Cereal (pg. 122) sprinkled on top! Yummm!

2 avocados

1 ripe banana

3 T raw cacao powder

2 T raw unfiltered honey

1 T pistachios

1 T pomegranate seeds

1. In a food processor or blender add avocados, banana, cacao powder and honey. Blend until smooth. Technically you can also grab a bowl and mix everything with your hands! As the avocados and banana are ripe it's pretty easy! (Plus you can lick your fingers afterwards!!)

2. Serve topped off with some pomegranate seeds (I love the crunchiness it gives to the mousse, but you can use any berry) and crushed pistachios, to add a salty kick!

CHOCO

AVOCADO
Mousse

KEFIR CHIA PUDDING

SERVES 1

This is one of my favorite ways to eat chia: making it into a pudding (besides being one of my top fave toppings for salads, smoothies, bowls, granola, and almost everything!!!). Again this is sooo easy and you can pre-batch in jars and store in your fridge to have as dessert, snack or even as an on-the-go breakfast! I experimented with this chia pudding after a weekend in New York where hubs had chia pudding for breakfast every day from a little juice bar on the corner. I found that using kefir (or your favorite yogurt with no added sugar, but remember kefir has more probiotics!) gives a more dense pudding, but you can use your favorite milk too! The prune preserve I use in this recipe is another experiment outcome; I once ran out of preserve for a blue cheese sandwich, so I came up with this! It's easy to make and lasts for a longggg time in the fridge stored in a jar! (I use dried plums because they are great for your digestion, plus I always have them in my pantry. I don't like making preserves from fresh fruit; in my humble opinion, if I have the fresh fruit I prefer having it fresh on top of toast or whenever I want the preserve!) So I always have a jar of Plum & Chia Preserve in my fridge for toasts, sandwiches and chia puddings!!

Feel free to make this chia pudding your style! Adding some pineapple purée, yummm, or your favorite fruits and goodies! I love adding nut butters because it adds some protein and I just love them!

1 cup kefir	1. Mix kefir and chia seeds, place in an airtight container and keep in the fridge overnight or for at least for 30 minutes.
3 T chia seeds	
1 T almond butter	
Mint	
Plum & Chia Preserve	2. Place plums in a bowl with filtered water and hydrate them for 15 minutes. Discard water and process in a food processor or blender. Mix in lime juice, chia seeds and honey and save in an airtight container in the fridge for up to 6 months. (As I mentioned earlier, this is the preserve I eat with my toasts, yogurt or oatmeal! Sooo yummy, easy and way cleaner than any store-bought preserves or jam!)
2 cups prunes	
2 T raw unfiltered honey	
3 T chia seeds	
2 limes (juice)	

3. In your favorite container pour some of the jelly-kefir-chia pudding mixture, then a layer of the plum preserve, then almond butter (or your favorite nut butter), and top it off with the remaining kefir and a mint leaf!

-KEFIR- Chia * PUDDING~

RAW & CRUNCHY SUPERFOOD BALLS

MAKES 6-8 BALLS

I can bet you may have seen similar-looking raw balls everywhere, but trust me, my take on this raw ball situation is incredibly yummy and so worth trying!! I've made pb balls with chocolate chips and others using dates and coconut, but these are by far my favorite!!! Why? In just one bite I get the crunchy, nutty and toasty flavor of the popped quinoa, sweetness of the goji berries and creaminess of the almond butter....do I have to say more? Ohh and it's loaded with superfoods!! So lots of nutrients, minerals and vitamins, that's a Smart Bite! Make a hundred and save them in an airtight container in the fridge for up to a month!! (Or even more! Check your almond butter expiration date!)

½ cup dry quinoa

¼ cup rolled oats

1 t spirulina

1 t cinnamon

1 t chia seeds

1 t hemp seeds

¼ cup goji berries

¼ cup almond butter

1 T raw honey

1. Place quinoa on a pan over medium heat. Stir quinoa until it starts popping (it doesn't pop like popcorn does, but if you pay attention you'll hear a little sound! And it can jump too!). Remove from the pan when it is golden brown. Let it cool down completely before continuing with other steps. (You can add this popped quinoa to your DIY Cereal (pg. 122), oatmeals and salads for a crunchy effect.)

2. In a bowl combine the dry ingredients: popped quinoa, rolled oats, spirulina, cinnamon, chia seeds, hemp seeds and goji berries. Mix well.

3. Add the wet ingredients into the bowl: almond butter and raw honey. Mix very well with your hands! (You know the trick; you can lick your fingers afterwards!!)

4. Form balls (1.5 inch diameter or the size you want!); if it's very sticky, water your hands a little.

5. Decorate with a goji berry on top, place in the fridge for 10 minutes and they are ready to enjoy!!

★ RAW & CRUNCHY SUPERFOOD BALLS ★

FLOURLESS HEMP BROWNIES

SERVES 12

I told you I love chocolate; obviously it goes hand in hand with brownies and these brownies are yumms! Plus super paleo (AKA low in carbs and sugars). Hubby always asks me to bake some for him (I always have some healthy treats at home for him to have with his coffee...so spoiled! And obviously for the sweet-toothed mommy-to-be too!!!). During my last week of pregnancy I think I ate these brownies every other day, and when we ran out I baked and baked and baked more!! These are easy to make; no fancy mixer needed here or anything, just a whisk and your strong arms!

3 whole eggs

⅓ cup milk/nut milk

⅓ cup coconut oil

1 T peanut butter

300 g/1 ½ cup sugar free chocolate chips or stevia-sweetened chocolate chips

1 cup stevia (if you use chocolate sweetened with stevia omit!)

⅔ cup cacao powder

1 cup almond meal

1 t aluminum-free baking powder

4 T hemp seeds + extra for topping

1. Preheat oven to 350°F or 177°C.

2. Place chocolate in a glass bowl. In 30-second intervals melt chocolate until smooth. Stir completely with a spatula each time (even if it doesn't look like it's melting, you need to distribute the heat!) ***Please NEVER use plastic containers in a microwave; it is toxic and bad for your body to eat food microwaved in plastic. I only use the microwave to melt chocolate and to store things! If you have to use it just remember to never use plastic.

3. To the melted chocolate add the coconut oil, peanut butter, milk and eggs. Stir very well with a spatula or whisk, using your strength!

4. To the new mixture add the dry ingredients: almond meal, stevia if needed, cacao powder, baking powder and hemp seeds.

5. Grease your baking molds a little with coconut oil before pouring in the mixture so they come out easily afterwards. You can

210

use your favorite baking molds (any muffin size works!). Pour mixture and bake for 15 minutes, no more than that! We want a soft center (if you insert a toothpick into the edges and it comes out clean, but the center is still a little raw, it is time!!!).

6. Unmold and let them cool down on a cooling rack (if you have one, if not just unmold them so they don't continue cooking!) and enjoy! Try not to eat them all; freshly baked they are even more irresistible.

CARROT-BANANA MUFFINS
(WITH CREAM CHEESE FROSTING)

MAKES 12 MUFFINS

I still remember the day I came up with this recipe (ok, the second try when I corrected one or two things); I thought to myself: "This is the best healthy baked goody I've ever made!!!" So, so yummy! As with my brownies, these could be considered "paleo" as well: no flour or sugar but only the best and smartest substitutions! (Smarty-pregnancy-pants!! Also no mixer needed!!) You can use this mixture for a rustic layer cake too, with the yummy cream cheese frosting in the middle! I recommend making the frosting the same day you are eating the muffins. The frosting will create the most drooling experience when freshly whipped! So if you are baking a batch you can save them in an airtight container in the fridge and then take 1 ½ minutes to freshly make the frosting! (FYI they taste amazing without the frosting too!!)

1 cup grated carrot

2 ripe bananas

½ cup milk/nut milk

3 T agave nectar

2 t apple cider vinegar

2 T coconut oil

2 eggs

2 cup almond flour/almond meal

⅔ cup old-fashioned oats

2 t aluminum-free baking powder

¼ t Himalayan pink salt

½ cup walnuts, chopped

6 dates, finely sliced

1. Preheat oven to 350°F or 177°C.

2. Prepare your muffin pan with cute paper cups or grease pan with coconut oil if not using paper cups.

3. In a bowl add grated carrot (processed finely in a food processor or blender), bananas, almond milk (or your favorite milk), agave nectar or maple syrup, apple cider vinegar, coconut oil and eggs. With your hands (or a whisk) mash the bananas and mix all ingredients.

4. Add dry ingredients to the bowl: almond flour, old-fashioned oats, baking powder, chopped walnuts and finely sliced dates. Mix until everything is well combined.

5. Pour mixture into paper cups and bake for 35 minutes (until you insert a toothpick and it comes out clean!)

Frosting

4 T cream cheese at room
temperature

2 T coconut oil

1 T maple syrup

1 date

cinnamon

6. Let muffins cool down on a cooling rack; if you don't have one just make sure you remove muffins from the pan so they don't continue cooking.

7. In a bowl whisk the cream cheese at room temperature (if you forgot to take it out from the fridge, warm it a little in a small pan) with the coconut oil and maple syrup.

8. Spread cream cheese frosting on muffins, decorate with date bits, sprinkle cinnamon and ta-da!!!

(with cream cheese frosting)

Carrot-Banana Muffins

IV. STAYING ACTIVE

STAYING ACTIVE

I cannot emphasize enough how important is to stay active during your whole pregnancy (and of course before if you are trying to conceive!); it goes hand in hand with healthy eating. Exercise helps you control your weight gain and your mood (during and after pregnancy! So we keep those baby blues far away!!!), and it even gives you a hand going into labor naturally (and makes it an easier labor!). For the baby it is awesome too! For instance, the placenta grows faster (oxygen, blood and nutrients being transferred to baby more efficiently!), plus baby loves being bounced around!...

Nonetheless, my advice is to follow a flexible schedule; the level, intensity and duration of your workouts depend a lot on your activity level before becoming pregnant. The most important thing is to stay very active in general: try to walk everywhere, take the stairs and do not make your belly an excuse!!! As I mentioned earlier if you can have a personal trainer go for it!! Or look for prenatal classes (Pilates or yoga) around your area; these classes, in addition to focusing on what you really need to work on, help you connect with other mommies-to-be! (We support each other and understand that all the weird stuff happening during this period is all normal!!!) I personally also loved working out at home, at my own pace and at a time I found more convenient.

So in my case, I attended prenatal yoga two or three times a week, I did full-body workouts at home, attended some Zumba classes (a group dancing class, but I did it at my own pace; no bouncing or jumping around!) and walked a lot!!! You will see that your workouts will be a little different according to the stage of pregnancy. Still I recommend you practice yoga, stretch and walk throughout the entire pregnancy (I'll show you some visuals ahead!); the intensity and duration is what mainly changes:

- During the **first trimester** you will feel very tired, but it's great to try to squeeze in some activity; it helps you with your morning sickness and boosts up your energy! You want to start your hip-opening exercises as soon as possible and do some full-body workouts to maintain your strong body!

- During the **second trimester** just go for it! You have the energy; your belly is still not that big so you can still make those Zumba moves! Continue with the hip-opening exercises and full-body workouts, and take advantage of the energy to really pump that heart!

- During the **last trimester** is great to really focus on those yoga poses and stretches to control all sorts of pain (back, leg and heartburn), and to really accentuate those hip-opening exercises and squats! (Remember they help induce labor.) Poses that take the weight off your back help your baby move into position for delivery (and give your back a break!). Also, walk like a lost person! During my last 2 weeks of pregnancy I walked every day or every other day from 45 minutes to an hour!

(Have in mind I'm not a professional and the following exercises are to be practiced at your own risk and pace; if you have extra concerns or questions ask your doctor or health practitioner!).

EVERYDAY YOGA POSES & STRETCHES

These poses are to do in a sequence or just whenever you feel you need them. For example, if a leg cramp wakes you up in the middle of the night, heartburn is killing you, or when your back hurts. During my last 2 weeks of pregnancy I tried focusing on poses where the belly was hanging (weight off the back) and on those hip-opening ones!

BUTTERFLY POSE *(hip-opening)*

Sit bringing the soles of your feet together. I start my yoga routine with this pose, a meditative pose.

I give thanks, set an intention and hold it for 10 breaths.

LATERAL STRETCH *(torso stretch)*

From a butterfly-seated position extend to one side and reach. Hold for 10 seconds for each side.

BABY SWING *(takes baby off back & back pain)*

Start in a tabletop position, open knees and arms hips-distance apart. Move forward like drawing a
wide circle with your belly, then back and around. Repeat 10 times.

CAT-COW POSE *(takes baby off back & back pain)*

Start in a tabletop position making sure knees are hip-distance apart and that knees, elbows and shoulders are in a line. Inhale and in the exhale round your back and tuck your chin (cat). Inhale and arch your back letting your belly relax (cow). Repeat the movement 10 times.

BALANCING CAT POSE *(strengthens abs & back muscles)*

Get on your hands and knees and extend opposite arm with opposite leg. Hold for 5 breaths. Repeat 3 times per side.

LEG CRAMP KILLER (leg cramp, pain & swollen legs)

Sit extending your legs and supporting yourself with your arms to the back.

Flex and extend your feet for 10 times or until you feel the leg cramp easing.

CAMEL POSE (heartburn & strengthens your back)

Kneel hip-distance apart, rest your hands on your back, inhale and on the exhale open your heart, move hips forward and start bending backwards with your chin up until you feel comfortable. If you are flexible enough rest your hands on your heels (be careful); if not just bend with your hands on your back, arch your back and let your head fall back. Hold the pose for 3 breaths and slowly come up.

CHILD'S POSE STRETCH *(hip-opening & back pain)*

Sit on your legs, open your knees making space for the belly, reach your hands to the front and rest forehead on the mat.

Hold pose for 5 breaths. Then slide one arm under your body and stretch for 30 seconds each side.

WARRIOR II POSE *(back PAIN, strengthens abs & legs)*

Open your legs, bend your front knee over your ankle, drop your back heel down to the mat turned 90° and face your hips

forward. Open your arms and look forward towards the middle of your fingers. Hold the pose for 8 breaths.

REVERSE WARRIOR POSE (stretches hips & strengthens legs)

From Warrior II Pose bring your back hand towards the back leg and stretch your other arm towards the sky.

Hold for 3 breaths.

ACTIVE WARRIOR POSE (hip-opening, leg & arm strengthening)

From Reverse Warrior Pose come back to Warrior II Pose and simultaneously stretch your front leg and move your arms up, holding for one breath and returning to the initial pose. Repeat sequence 5 times, holding in Warrior II Pose for 3 breaths each time for each side

SIDE ANGLE POSE *(hip-opening & back pain)*

Open your legs, bend your front knee over your ankle, drop your back heel down to the mat turned 90° and face your hips forward (Warrior II Pose). Bend forward and rest your elbow on your knee. Make sure knee is over your feet and extend upper arm above your head. Hold for 5 breaths each side.

HEART OPENING & FORWARD BEND *(heartburn & back pain)*

Open your legs wide, interlace your fingers to the back and let your head fall back opening your chest. Hold for 3 breaths, then slowly fall forward for 3 more breaths.

GODDESS POSE (stretch legs & open hips)

Open your legs wide apart, your feet looking out, and with your back straight bend your knees; if you want rest your hands in your knees pushing a little to deepen the stretch. Hold for 5 breaths.

WIDE SQUAT (super hip-opening!)

Open your feet a little more than hip-distance, and lower your hips as far down as you can go. Press your knees out with your elbows, keeping hands in prayer position. Hold for 5 breaths. Do this pose every day for your whole pregnancy, especially if you want to get flexible for a natural birth; it makes more room in the pelvis!!

LEG STRETCH (stretch legs & open hips)

Fold one knee and extend the other leg pointing your toes up. Hold for 8 breaths per side.

and to keep those muscles nice & tone...

Easy WORKOUT ROUTINES

ARMS

We want to work our arms to keep them in nice shape, but most importantly we need them strong to be able to hold our babies! (and carry the diaper bag, purse and groceries, and for folding and unfolding your stroller!!). For each exercise do 15 reps 3 times, resting as much as you need to in between!

Triceps

Shoulders

Raise arm until shoulder level alternating arms

Shoulders

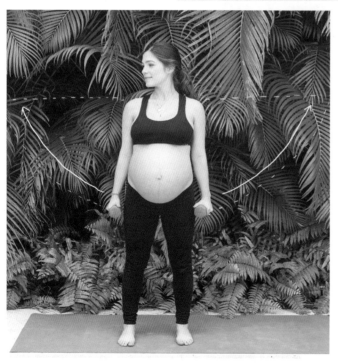

231

BUTT & LEGS

We also want to continue working our butt and legs; we don't only want to feel good and sexy, but also get the strength to support the belly weight and to be able to use our legs (not our backs) when picking something up (a strong lower body also makes an easier natural birth delivery!). For each exercise do 15 reps (for each side when applied) 3 times, resting as much as you need to in between!

1.

2.

Squats

SUMO Squats

MEDITATION

I consider meditation a crucial piece in the puzzle of pregnancy. It doesn't only help you reinforce that connection between you and your baby, but it also helps you survive your aches, sleepless nights of discomfort and anxiety, as well as prepare you for your big day! Plus you can use some of these techniques during labor!!

I recommend setting aside at least 5 minutes of your day to sit in a quiet place and just concentrate on relaxing (do it in the morning, before bed, or as the secret weapon when you can't fall asleep!!!); you can play some music, follow a guided meditation (which can be found online or is usually part of your prenatal yoga class) or repeat a mantra (a mantra is a phrase or word repeated to help you concentrate during meditation. The most common example is "ommmm"). You can actually come up with your own mantra, which can be modified according to how you are feeling (weak, nervous, anxious, etc.). For example: "We are blessed, we are strong, we are healthy and happy;" "Strong mom, strong baby." My prenatal yoga teacher (Debra Geymayr, RPYT, E-RYT, HBCE, CD(DONA), CLD, CPD, CHBE, OSD, IMP, CPE. Prenatal Yoga Plus) taught me the following mantra: "My baby and I are Happy, Healthy and Holy," to be repeated with one hand on your heart and the other on your belly. You won't believe how magical this simple action becomes. In addition to these you can also use visualization. For example, visualizing the moment when you will first hold your baby, picturing everything turning out great, seeing him healthy, perfect and happy!

We are BLESSED,
we are STRONG,
We are HEALTHY
& HAPPY

♥Romantic LIFE

This is a MAJOR concern during pregnancy so let's just jump into it! There are lots of things happening with you, lots of changes, new things and those horrible hormones that sometimes make us nuts! So as crazy as it may sound, you need to put yourself in your significant other's shoes and stop the craziness. I've heard stories of pregnant women who can't stand the smell of their partner and others that end up sleeping apart! I don't know what you think about it, but for me that's nonsense!! You need to stay together, support each other, be tolerant of both sides, and enjoy the experience! It goes by sooo fast! Plus you need to be extra close and in tune when your baby arrives! (That is the challenging part!) I know you feel extra sensitive and want to be pampered and pleased all the time, but let's just not cross the line! Be intelligent and use your situation to your advantage! From my experience I can tell you that if you follow a healthy (mentally and foodwise) and active pregnancy, you'll have a totally awesome experience and the craziness level and mood swings won't be that much of an issue (hubby can prove it!). You need to be chill and relax! That energy is also felt by your little one!

And what about SEX? I won't lie, I was also a little concerned about the safety of my baby (would he get poked? LOL), but the truth is that sex is totally safe and beneficial to you, your baby and your partner! (Unless you experience bleeding or abnormal pain. Consult your doctor immediately.) So let me break it down for you: during your first trimester you may be feeling soooo tired and weird, and sometimes cramps get in the way, so be patient, discuss how you feel with your partner and work it out together! During your second trimester your energy is back, yayyy you feel kind of normal, plus they say you are more sensitive because of the increased blood flow down there! So take advantage of the situation, spice it up and catch up! Lastly, during your third trimester your energy levels will lower a little again plus your belly will now be on the way, so embrace it and find comfortable positions and work with what you have! You must know that sex is a natural labor inducer!! (So those last weeks when you feel you just want your baby out, put your partner to work!!)

So to sum up, my advice is to really stick together throughout the whole process, be tolerant and really enjoy every moment! If you don't feel like having sex one day, maybe because you are tired or for some reason your sex drive is lower, just remember your partner is not pregnant! Of course they are up to it! So just show them some love! Don't be selfish (I know you know one or two ways to do that!). Take showers together, hug and kiss a lot, give each other massages, take some spooned naps and movie nights... you need to work it out to keep it spicy! Even if it's not all-the-way lovemaking, that will keep you both going throughout these nine months!

V. Preparing for baby's arrival

PETS AND BABY'S ARRIVAL

Enzo and Vera are the names of our cute pups. We had planned them to be our only babies for a little longer! As hubby and I grew up with dogs we wanted the same experience for our little boy; if that's also your case take a look at these tips to make the process smoother, especially for your four-legged babies who are the ones soon to be dethroned:

- It's incredible how they know something is going on with you! During my first trimester, when I felt really tired, they were a lot calmer than they used to be and followed me everywhere! (more than usual). And of course they loved napping with me every day! So just talk to them and explain there is a sibling coming to the house very soon. (They may not understand the words but they sense the energy you are transmitting to them when talking!)

- Play crying baby sounds to get them used to those new sounds. (The baby won't mind about the barking; he will have been hearing them for 9 months through your belly!)

- When your baby is born send a hat and a blanket or anything the baby has worn and has his smell with a relative for the dogs to smell before the baby comes home. This way, they will recognize the smell once the baby is home!

- Have treats and a toy ready for the day you come home from the hospital with the baby. That will be the gift from their new sibling that they will love!

- Tell daddy he will need to pay extra attention to your pups as you are going to have your hands more than full with your newborn. Even if you really don't want to, it's inevitable that you'll be a little apart from your pets during the first few weeks. Babies take most of your time, plus they are very delicate with their immune systems just being built up! (especially the first 2 months). Remember, as clean as your pets are, they are still cute animals!

REGISTRY LISTS 101

My take on the registry list was to go for the most basic and really necessary things (trust me there are tons of things that will look necessary and essential but they are not really. Especially nowadays with all those new products that they want to sell us all the time). You don't want to fill up your home storage space with tchotchkes! So go with the basics first, and along the way buy the things you find you are missing! For specific brands on products I bought, follow our extra goodies link!

NURSERY BASICS

- [ ] Co-sleeper (bassinet)
- [ ] Crib
- [ ] Organic mattress
- [ ] Mattress cover
- [ ] Organic sheets
- [ ] Dresser
- [ ] Changing table
- [ ] Changing pad
- [ ] Changing pad cover
- [ ] Rocking chair
- [ ] Storage bins/shelves
- [ ] Monitor
- [ ] White noise machine

MAIN GEAR

- [ ] Car seat
- [ ] Stroller
- [ ] Travel stroller
- [ ] Pack-n-play
- [ ] Bouncing chair
- [ ] Sleeper seat
- [ ] Activity gym
- [ ] Diaper bag
- [ ] Baby carrier

FEEDING

- [ ] Breast pump
- [ ] Nursing pillow
- [ ] BPA-free bottles
- [ ] Bottle sterilizer
- [ ] Bottle warmer
- [ ] Drying rack
- [ ] High chair
- [ ] Organic cotton bibs

BATH & HEALTH

- [ ] Infant tub
- [ ] Hooded towel
- [ ] Washcloths
- [ ] Natural baby wash
- [ ] Rinse cup
- [ ] Nasal aspirator
- [ ] Thermometer
- [ ] Medicine syringe
- [ ] Manicure set
- [ ] Wipes warmer

TOYS

- [ ] Rattles
- [ ] Bath toys
- [ ] Teething toys
- [ ] Mobile

Follow our ★ EXTRA ★ ★ GOODIES ★ link to download! ★ WWW.FFTHMIAMI.COM/ EXTRA - GOODIES

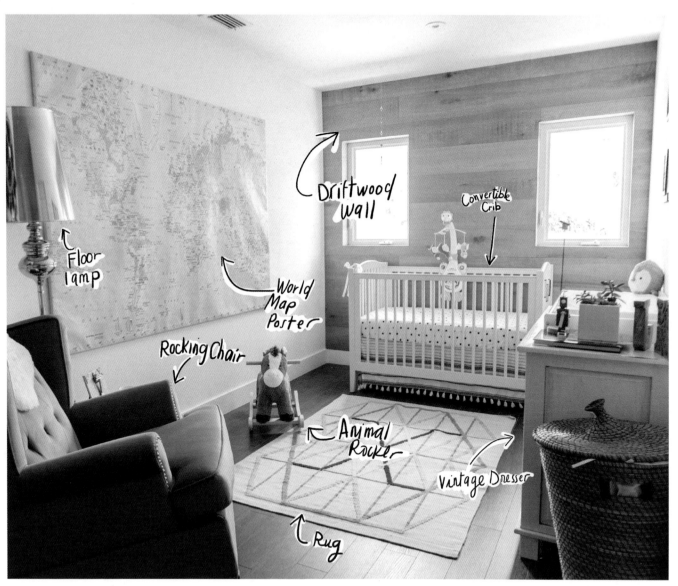

Driftwood Wall

Convertible Crib

Floor lamp

World Map Poster

Rocking Chair

Animal Rocker

Vintage Dresser

Rug

Rustic-Gender-Neutral Nursery

BABY SHOWER
INSPIRATION

I didn't want to go with the traditional baby blue
or pink baby shower with diaper cakes and bottles
everywhere (not that there is anything wrong with
those; they can actually be pretty cute!), but instead
I wanted something different and more gender-neu-
tral. I'll show you some ideas and DIY's from my
woodland baby shower that could easily be adapted
for a more girly mood if desired. I absolutely love
the boho-natural-woodsy vibes that you can get from
this theme!

Some DIY's ahead!

246

It's A

Beautiful

- DAY -

Mirror artwork by @cr_eatestudio

Sparkling water
+
Coconut Water
+
Frozen Pineapple
+
Homegrown Basil

FLAVORED WATER

248

Real succulents

Real feathers

Figurine

CAKE TOPPER

1. Paper Bag

2. Put Banana Bread Bites in!

3. Close with washi tape

4. Chalkboard marker write "Thank you" on a chalkboard tag

5. Glue gun paste feather on the back of the tag

6. Glue gun paste tag on the closed bag!

Baby Shower

in honor of...

- -

You are invited...

Follow our ★ EXTRA ★ ★ GOODIES ★ link to ★ download! ★ WWW. FFTHMIAMI.COM/ EXTRA-GOODIES

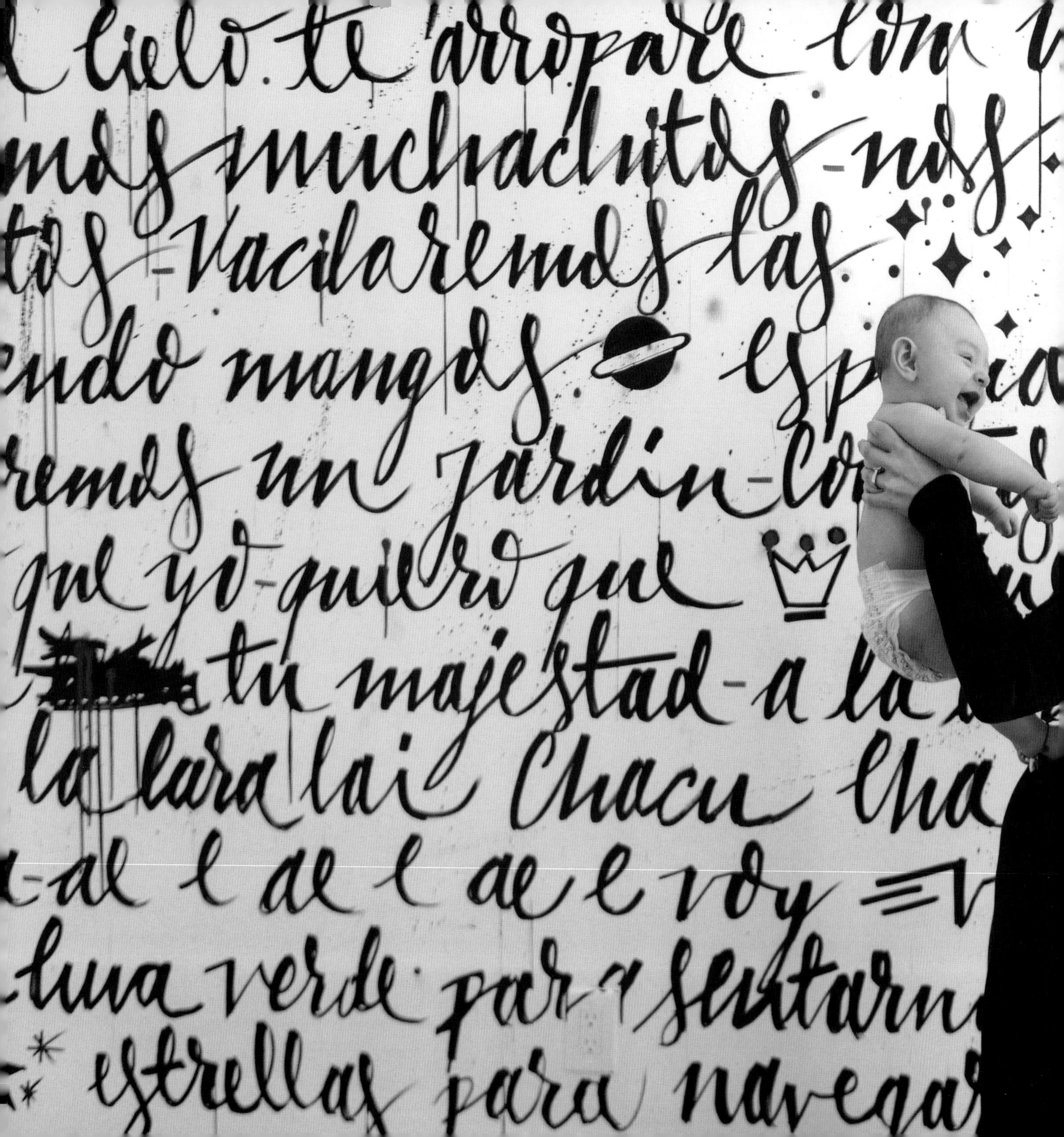

l cielo te arropare con

mas muchachitos nos

tos Vacilaremos las

ndo mangos espe

remos un jardin co

que yo quiero que

tu majestad a la

la lara lai Chacu cha

al e al e ae e voy

lua verde par sentar

estrellas para navega

Olafsdottir, A. S., Magnusardottir, A. R., Thorgeirsdottir, H., Hauksson, A., Skuladottir, G. V. & Steingrimsdottir, L. (2005). Relationship between dietary intake of cod liver oil in early pregnancy and birthweight. BJOG: An International Journal of Obstetrics & Gynaecology, 112(4), 424–429.

Planck, Nina. (2009). Real food for mother and baby: The fertility diet, eating for two, and baby's first foods. New York, NY: Bloomsbury USA.

Robinson, J. (2004). Pasture perfect: How you can benefit from choosing meat, eggs, and dairy products from grass-fed animals. Vashon, WA: Vashon Island Press.

Romm, A. J. (2003). The natural pregnancy book: Herbs, nutrition, and other holistic choices. Berkeley, CA: Celestial Arts.

Rosenthal, J. (2007). Integrative nutrition: Feed your hunger for health and happiness. New York, NY: Integrative Nutrition Pub.

The Science of Eating. (2015, December 28). 6 Simple tricks to remove pesticides from your food (and detox your body). Retrieved from http://thescienceofeating.com/2015/12/28/6-simple-tricks-to-remove-pesticides-from-your-food-and-detox-your-body/

Smith, B. L. (1993). Organic foods vs supermarket foods: Element levels. Journal of Applied Nutrition, 45(1): 35-39. Retrieved from https://www.researchgate.net/publication/238095026_Organic_Foods_vs_Supermarket_Foods_Element_Levels

U.S. Food and Drug Administration. (2003). Quantitative assessment of relative risk to public health from foodborne Listeria monocytogenes among selected categories of ready-to-eat foods. US Food and Drug Administration Center for Food Safety and Applied Nutrition, College Park, MD. Retrieved from http://www.fda.gov/Food/FoodScienceResearch/RiskSafetyAssessment/ucm183966.htm

Weil, A. (2013). Are frozen vegetables healthy? - Ask Dr. Weil. Retrieved from http://www.drweil.com/diet-nutrition/nutrition/are-frozen-vegetables-healthy/

World Cancer Research Fund International. (2015). Curbing global sugar consumption: Effective food policy actions to help promote healthy diets and tackle obesity. Retrieved from http://www.wcrf.org/sites/default/files/Curbing-Global-Sugar-Consumption.pdf

BIBLIOGRAPHY

American Cancer Society. (2016). Teflon and Perfluorooctanoic Acid (PFOA). Retrieved from http://www.cancer.org/cancer/cancercauses/othercarcinogens/athome/teflon-and-perfluorooctanoic-acid--pfoa

American Pregnancy Association. (2015). Pregnancy weight gain. Retrieved from http://americanpregnancy.org/pregnancy-health/pregnancy-weight-gain/

Bánhidy, F., Lowry, R. B., & Czeizel, A. E. (2005). Risk and benefit of drug use during pregnancy. International Journal of Medical Sciences, 2(3), 100-106. http://doi:10.7150/ijms.2.100

Benbrook, C., Zhao, X., Yáñez, J., Davies, N., & Andrews, P. (2008). New evidence confirms the nutritional superiority of plant-based organic foods. The Organic Center: Foster, RI. Retrieved from https://www.organic-center.org/reportfiles/Nutrient_Content_SSR_FINAL_V2.pdf

Beyerlein, A., Schiessl, B., Lack, N., & von Kries, R. (2009). Optimal gestational weight gain ranges for the avoidance of adverse birth weight outcomes: A novel approach. The American Journal of Clinical Nutrition, 90(6), 1552-1558. http://doi:10.3945/ajcn.2009.28026

Boston Women's Health Book Collective. (2008). Our bodies, ourselves: Pregnancy and birth. Boston, MA: Simon & Schuster, Inc.

Environmental Working Group. (2016). EWG's 2016 Shopper's guide to pesticides in produce. Retrieved from https://www.ewg.org/foodnews/about.php

Environmental Working Group. (n.d.). EWG healthy home tips: Tip 6 - Skip the non-stick to avoid the dangers of teflon. Retrieved from http://www.ewg.org/research/healthy-home-tips/tip-6-skip-non-stick-avoid-dangers-teflon

Evans, J. & Aronson, R. (2005). The whole pregnancy handbook: An obstetrician's guide to integrating conventional and alternative medicine before, during, and after pregnancy. New York, NY: Penguin Group, Inc.

Fenichel, P., Chevalier, N., & Brucker-Davis, F. (2013). Bisphenol A: An endocrine and metabolic disruptor. Annales D'Endocrinologie, 74(3), 211-20. http://doi:10.1016/j.ando.2013.04.002

Fretz, R., Sagel, U., Ruppitsch, W., Pietzka, A. T., Stöger, A., Huhulescu, S., . . . & Allerberger, F. (2010). Listeriosis outbreak caused by acid curd cheese 'Quargel', Austria and Germany 2009. Euro Surveillance, 15(5). Retrieved from http://www.eurosurveillance.org/ViewArticle.aspx?ArticleId=19477

Gawain, S. (1999). The four levels of healing: A guide to balancing the spiritual, mental, emotional, and physical aspects of life. Novato, CA: New World Library.

Gebhardt, S. E., & Thomas, R. G. (2002). Nutritive value of foods. Home and Garden Bulletin 72. Beltsville, MD: U.S. Department of Agriculture, Agricultural Research Service.

GRACE Communications Foundation. (2016). Welcome to sustainable table. Retrieved from http://www.sustainabletable.org/

Hari, V., & Hyman, M. H. (2016). The food babe way: Break free from the hidden toxins in your food and lose weight, look years younger, and get healthy in just 21 days!. New York, NY: Little, Brown and Company.

Nabisco. (n.d.). Nabisco 100 Calorie Packs Oreo Thin Crisps 0.81 Oz. Retrieved from http://www.snackworks.com/products/product-detail.aspx?product=4400000617

13 WEEKS
POST-PARTUM
Mural by
@cr_eatestudio

Thank you! ♡

Show us some love
by sharing your experience
#pregancyfromtheheart

www.ffthmiami.com